◆◦§◦◆

THE ESSENTIAL GUIDE TO
EROTIC LITERATURE
PART TWO

THE ESSENTIAL GUIDE TO EROTIC LITERATURE

PART TWO
After 1920

CLIFFORD J. SCHEINER MD

WORDSWORTH CLASSICS

This edition published 1996 by
Wordsworth Editions Limited
Cumberland House, Crib Street
Ware, Hertfordshire SG12 9ET

ISBN 1 85326 631 0

Typeset by Antony Gray
Printed and bound in Great Britain by
Mackays of Chatham plc, Chatham, Kent

Introduction

This book is not a history of erotic literature. Nor is it a bibliography of erotica. It is rather an anthology of extracts from specific works of erotic literature which I find are exemplars of the numerous functions which erotica serves.

Erotica is, and should be, fun. Since time immemorial, sexually explicit literature has served the multiple purposes of education, aphrodisia *and* entertainment. In just the recent past it has been recognised by scholars, academics and social researchers that this self-same material is also a valuable and legitimate source of primary reference. While this acceptance should in no way diminish the pure joy of erotica, it does expand its cultural significance and acknowledge its redeeming social value.

Not that there is anything wrong with pure and simple entertainment. I hope that my readers will find the following texts pleasurable. However, as has been recognised by formal academia, erotic literature does have much more to offer, and in acknowledgement of this, there has been created a formal academic discipline, called erotology, under which the scholarly study of erotic material is classified. This present work was in fact first created to be a course curriculum for graduate study, and was amended for the purposes of a broader, less pedantic audience.

Erotology is a multidisciplinary field. Its primary concern is the collection and investigation of all manner of expression concerned with sex. This includes not only the actual physical act of procreation, but the attitudes towards it, the social and cultural controls on it, the depictions of it in art and literature, the psychology and physiology (i.e. mind and body) at all levels of physical and mental complexity to explain the instigation and successful completion of copulation, and the artifices (aphrodisiacs) used to promote sexual activity. Erotology concerns itself with the real and tangible, as well as the symbolic and surrogate. Art, science, law, economy, criminology, theology, sociology, medicine, linguistics, ethnology and history are just a few of the 'major' academic disciplines that are readily identifiable as being concerned with the subject matter of erotology. Since the primary inborn, genetic instinct of the human being is successfully to reproduce its species, it is obvious that no element of human life is without sexual elements. It is the understanding of the evolution and expression of these sexual elements that is the foundation of erotology.

The largest fund of primary erotological source material is the collective sum of human activity throughout the entirety of history. The libido is the primary mental drive of the organism, to which all other drives and instincts, including the will to survive, subserviate themselves. Therefore, everything that mankind has ever done has at some time been done with a sexual connotation, or in an attempt to enhance the frequency, efficiency or pleasure of sexual activity. Most of this material has been lost due to lack of documentation, and even that which has been recorded in word and picture and archetypal memory is too vast to analyse in full. The purpose of this project is to create a defined collection of written literature (as opposed to material that survives only in the oral tradition or in non-verbal forms of expression) that will serve as an introductory text to the varied forms of erotological material. Additionally, the material will be for the most part limited to original works, rather than compilations of earlier material, of sufficient length to be considered equivalent to the modern 'novel', although both fiction and non-fiction is included.

The 'literature' of erotology is without calculable bounds and stretches from the beginning of physically recorded language. If 'a picture is worth a thousand words', then symbolically, this literature extends back in time to the earliest drawings of *homo sapiens*, since the earliest uttered verbal communications of mankind are now lost to history. Over the millennia erotological representations have been in the form of spoken and recorded words, physical actions, pictures, music, dance, sculpture, 'art' of every sort, written words, photographs, movies, videos, and every other form of communication that has ever existed, or with the assistance of science and technology, ever will. The 'literature' of erotology, the written words, have been in the form of puns, one liners, jokes, riddles, acrostics, novels, short stories, anecdotes, epigrams, anagrams, ballads, songs, plays, drama, poems, fiction, non-fiction, captions, etc. In other words, every form of prose and verse has been applied to matters of sexual expression. Even mixed media, such as rebuses, have their place in the canon of erotology.

This particular book is limiting itself to what might be generically referred to as 'formal' erotic literature. By my own subjective definition this means works that have been printed and are equivalent in length to what we commonly refer to as a 'novel'. This in no way makes a value judgement as to the validity or scientific importance of ephemeral and shorter material, nor claims any superiority of one form over another for the purposes of erotological research. This decision is simply made to allow the creation of a specific original contribution to the field of erotology that will have the defined purpose of being used as an introductory text to this specific aspect of erotology. It should be remembered that as early as the fifteenth century, Antonio Beccatolli scoured the extant writings from ancient Greek and Roman times, and excerpted all found references to sexual practices. This unpublished manuscript was rediscovered in the nineteenth century by Friedrich Karl Forberg, who edited and expanded the text, added his own commentary, and published it in Latin in 1824 as *Hermaphroditus* by Panormitae. This work is best known to the world today under the title of its English translation, printed by Nichols and Smithers in 1887: *The Manual of Classical Erotology*.

For this book, selections from the *œuvre* of erotic literature have been arranged chronologically, and were chosen to be representative of the function and form of erotic literature through history. This anthology is not exhaustive in scope, nor is it meant to be. The selections demonstrate the various themes and styles that have been penned and preserved for us as erotic literature, and are extant for evaluation and analysis. While most pieces are fiction prose, allowances have been made for the various forms of literature that predominated at different periods of time. Non-prose pieces and non-fiction considered to be seminal examples of erotica were included if they equally represented the popular form of literature of their times.

The titles that have been chosen for this guide are all classics of erotica. They express in fact or fantasy the psychological and cultural content of the sexual psyche of the society that produced the text. As much as some wish to believe that the content of sexually explicit writing, and erotic literature in particular, is all fantasy, the truth is that this genre expresses the 'nuts and bolts' of daily social life, the unglamorous tasks of daily living, that is most often omitted from the conventional, 'official', formal literature of the day. Where else is to be found the historical record of personal hygiene and copulation and conception and birth, sexual colloquialisms (slang), actual sexual practices as opposed to the expressed morality of the age, libidinal fantasies, venereal health concerns, undergarments, fetishes, aphrodisiacs, and the homeopathy and folklore and distortions of the sexual impulse? This literature may be *sub rosa*, but it is from the underbelly of the mind that the motivating forces behind civilisation arise.

The original incarnation of this work, as a course curriculum, was intended to present to the academic, professional and lay communities a body of work which demonstrated what erotology was, in terms of being a serious and indispensable research discipline for all other academic disciplines to borrow from, since it is a unique repository of vital information on the physical and psychological 'facts' that have been suppressed, censored, bowdlerised and otherwise omitted in true form from other genres. Throughout history, until the mid twentieth century, it has been the rare exception where overtly explicit sexual material, visual or otherwise, has been allowed to be openly published, even in the scientific and serious medium of dissertations or studies. For example, when the extremely important and massive collection of English ballads known as *Bishop Percy's Folio* was being prepared for publication during Victorian times, the editors had to remove those pieces with sexual content, and privately publish them separately as the infamous 'fourth volume'. When the compilers of the great Oxford English Dictionary, the largest etymological and lexicographical undertaking in history, decided against including sexual slang and 'dirty words' in their 'complete' reference, it fell to John S. Farmer and William Henley to gather these common terms and privately publish their eight-volume result, *Slang and Its Analogues*, as a proper supplement to the *Oxford English Dictionary*.

Since this current book is meant to be published and widely distributed, certain unfortunate realities of our times had to be considered to avoid limitation of its distribution. Current national laws for the most part place limitations on even written depictions of sadomasochism, bestiality, anal sex, paedophilia (sex with persons under the age of legal consent) and incest. Suspected 'intent' (a purely subjective, capricious and arbitrary assessment, usually made by individuals with no special expertise in the subject matter being considered) is paramount in the decision to censor and suppress material. We are aware that all the 'banned' sexual topics are in fact descriptions of activities that occur naturally and frequently in the real world, with different levels of social and legal acceptability at different geographic locales and times in history. To discuss sexual life or sexual literature without reference to these forbidden behaviours is like trying to describe what a stew is, without any mention of the vegetables! Additionally, as mores change over the centuries, what was usual and acceptable at one time, becomes criminal at another. Current national laws make the age of sexual consent sixteen. Yet when the average lifespan for the human being was twenty-five, and not seventy-five as today, this limitation could have doomed the human species. The Old Testament reflected this when it pronounced a female ready for marriage (legal sexual intercourse) when menstruation began. This thinking is still prevalent in parts of our world today, but not in Europe or the United States. Equally, flagellation, which we contemporarily classify as a form of sadomaso-chism, was once widely and openly practised, especially for its aphrodisiac effects. Revisionist thinking and George Orwell's *Nineteen Eighty-Four* aside, the authentic writings of bygone times do not change spontane-ously to suit our current mores and laws.

To falsify or rewrite literature to satisfy temporal, and soon to change, moral and legal proscriptions is a crime against honesty, integrity and the scientific foundation upon which all proper research must be conducted. To do so would also defeat the entire purpose of this project, which is to present historical *evidence*, in the form of a body of literature, that is truthful and valid primary material for analysis to discover sexual truths that have been preserved for us over the millennia.

Practical considerations must be maintained. The extant library of erotic literature is so vast that 'mild' and legally acceptable depictions of most sexual activity (except 'kiddie porn') exist, and those have been specifically chosen for inclusion here. Where stated ages of characters would contravene legal statutes, yet the descriptions of the characters clearly indicate them to be mature, consenting adults, the ages have been simply omitted. The latitude I am allowed in making the excerpt choices to achieve the stated goal is immense. Perhaps at a later date another curriculum, to be strictly limited to recognised professionals as defined by law, will be compiled to make available for serious scientific research erotological material felt to be inappropriate for the general public, but still of extreme and vital importance to our understanding of the history, forms and expressions, social attitudes and control of actual acts and fantasies that are now considered psychopathological and sexually criminal.

Erotology, the study of things erotic (i.e. concerning sexual stimulation and activity), is solidly based in the sociology of its time. The importance of written erotological material as a research tool is that it accurately reflects the actual *sub rosa* actions and thoughts of the culture, society, or population that produced and read it. From four-thousand-year-old Egyptian papyri recording sexual dreams (replete with incest and genital mutilations) to the current 'bestsellers' list, with examples like *American Psycho*, we see that very little has actually changed in the way human beings think about and act out the sexual impulse. We know that the natural mechanisms of human reproduction, as well as the inborn instincts and neural reflexes controlling it, have not altered. Equally, the symbolic expressions of sexual thoughts and acts have altered little since the beginning of recorded history. Mankind has remained, in Freud's words, the same polymorphous perverse creature that was created by millions of years of evolution that defied any concept of morality or social control. The proof is in the records erotologists discover and elucidate. Erotic literature purely reflects the society from which it emanated; it does not shape or change it, as is the purpose of philosophical and theological texts. History researches actions, philology researches literature and language, philosophy studies thought, teleology and ontology study the origins and meanings of reality. Erotology studies all of these in their service of the libido, the life-force principle that directs mankind to preserve its species and culture.

Erotology is not abstract. It is not a hypothetical science; without people, it cannot exist (unlike mathematics, biology, physics and sciences that objectively exist, irrespective of the existence of living, breathing, conscious human beings). The richness and value of erotic literature is enhanced and more apparent when the facts of its creation are known, as well as the social circumstances in which it was nascent. The bibliography of the work is necessary for understanding the social implications of the text, and vice versa.

That is the explanation for the form I have chosen in which to present this work. Classic, representative examples of erotic literature have been chosen, and arranged in chronological order. A socio-critico-bibliographical preface is given to establish a social context for the excerpt which follows. The excerpt has been extracted from the full text of the work and may have been slightly edited (but never censored or bowdlerised or changed in context) to satisfy current standards for international distribution.

CONTENTS

I

My Life and Loves
FRANK HARRIS 1922–7

The most notorious memoir of the twentieth century has been, since 1922, Frank Harris's *My Life and Loves*. No other autobiography of this century has met with such private and public condemnation, censorship, bowdlerisation, criminal prosecution and financial success. Individuals on both sides of the Atlantic have actually been jailed because of its publication, sale and possession. For years it ranked as the book most smuggled out of Paris by tourists.

In the annals of erotic literature Harris's work bears comparison to only two other works. The first is the nineteenth-century sexual autobiography *My Secret Life* by the anonymous 'Walter', a book that is frequently confused with *My Life and Loves*. *My Secret Life* is, for the most part, a clinical recitation of its author's sexual affairs, and concentrates on little else of a more profound nature. Harris, on the other hand, gives a much greater social and political account of his times and acquaintances, and happens to add in a few sexually explicit chapters. As such it equates more with Casanova's eighteenth-century *Memoirs*. Casanova was an adventurer and a spy; he also liked the ladies and uninhibitedly wrote of them in his life story. Harris was a writer and editor, as well as an adventurer and world traveller who liked the ladies, and . . .

It was Harris's personality that gave his autobiography notoriety beyond its deserve. Harris was an unmitigated egotist; he was also the most brilliant editor that England had seen in centuries. He had a personable, popular style, that placed everything in social contexts. He also had the reputation as a rascal and scoundrel, and perhaps a bit of a liar. He was fearless to the point of being foolhardy. It is said that he was invited to every great house in England, but only once. He enraged the British nation by criticising the sacrosanct military hero General

Charles 'Chinese' Gordon – of Khartoum fame; and infuriated the Churchill family by recounting how Lord Randolph (a perennially high-ranking member of the British government, and the father of Sir Winston) caught syphilis from a common strumpet! He condemned the English position in the Boer War, and stood up to the powerful Cecil Rhodes. He got away with it, and his audience loved him for it.

Harris was born into an undistinguished Irish family in 1855. After school in Ireland and England he took himself to America and became a cowboy, displaying the recklessness that was to be his hallmark for life. But his genius was writing. At the age of twenty-seven he became editor of his first magazine; he had his second three years later. At thirty-eight he became owner and editor of the comatose *Saturday Review*, and turned it into the finest and most influential journal of its day. He edited four more magazines in his career, including the famous *Pearson's*. In addition he found time to be a novelist, short-story writer, playwright, poet and biographer. (Many say that his best work was on the life of Oscar Wilde.) All this while he continued to travel extensively.

In his capacity as editor of prestigious publications, he hob-nobbed with the important political, social and artistic figures of his day; even royalty were numbered among his personal acquaintances. For his part, he was dynamic and mesmerising, a connoisseur and a lover of many beautiful women. He had access to the juiciest gossip of the day, and was not particularly discreet with it. After all, he realised, what made him so successful as an editor was that he gave the people what they really wanted – scandal, controversy and SEX. In return, the influence of his magazines provided him any protection he needed from his enemies.

Walter Galligher, in his introduction to the Grove Press 'complete and unexpurgated' edition of *My Life and Loves* stated, 'Had Frank Harris died in 1914 . . . he would be known to us first as the incomparable editor of the *Saturday Review* and friend of Oscar Wilde, and then as a writer.' In other words, he would now be a forgotten footnote in history! What immortalised Harris was his egotistical, almost asinine, attempt to write 'the most honest autobiography ever penned'. Like Casanova and Rousseau before him, he is sadly remembered most for the sex scenes, while the balance of the rich tableaux of history he recorded is forgotten.

One should not feel sorry for Harris. He knew exactly what he was doing with *My Life and Loves*. Starting in 1922 he self published the first four volumes over a six-year period in a small private edition from his home in France. The 'sexy' parts of the books were actually paginated separately; cynics said that this was so his audience could find them more easily, while Harris insisted that it was only so they could more easily be removed from copies to be exported to Puritan climes. For America, a specially edited edition was prepared and published in New York by Esar Levine, who went to jail anyway for his efforts. Meanwhile pirate editions of *My Life and Loves* sprang up like wildfire. In 1931 there even appeared a book entitled *My Love Life* which was, for the most part, just the racy parts.

Harris died in 1931, but his 'fame' spread as his autobiography became an underground bestseller. In America the *sub-rosa* pornography market kept Harris's words always available for sale. In Europe his four volumes could be legally bought in Paris, as Harris had signed a contract with the Obelisk Press, run by Jack Kahane, the father of Maurice Girodias. The 'New Freedom' of the 1960s finally allowed for a legal, unexpurgated edition of *My Life and Loves* to be printed in the United States, and Grove Press issued it (excellently edited and referenced and indexed). Twenty-three years after his death, an 'apocryphal' fifth volume to the Harris autobiography was created by Girodias and Alex Trocchi, loosely based around a few typed sheets left by Harris at his death.

Here then is a sample of the genuine 'racy bits' that have given *My Life and Loves* its classic status. Modern readers will wonder what all the fuss has been about, especially when the 1920s text is compared to its 1950s imitation. However, legends die hard.

ᕫ᠆᠆ from *My Life and Loves*

My first visit to Japan, nearly half a century ago now, was one of intense enjoyment. I was interested almost at once as I have never been interested anywhere else. Almost immediately I grasped the main fact that the people were freer of morality than even the French. I meant to stay a month and stayed nearly six: I went all the way up the inland sea and began. I think, to understand that great people in most of its idiosyncrasies.

The first thing that struck me wherever I went in Japan was the astonishing politeness and courtesy of the people. To enter either a hotel or an inn was a real pleasure; everyone seemed glad to see you and the little waitresses were smiling with pleasure and delighted to do whatever they could for you. Japan has been called the land of flowers. It is also the land of the most tender and passionate of women. My first experience, which brought home to me the truth of my last remark, took place only one day after I arrived and it was with one of the pretty waitresses who, from the moment I entered the hotel, did their utmost to make my stay a pleasant one.

It was the waitress who served at my own table in the dining room who appeared on the morning after my arrival at my bedside with the loaded breakfast tray. I had retired late, having talked far into the night with a friend, and I had left instructions with the desk clerk for my breakfast to be served in my room at ten o'clock.

I woke up with the curtains being drawn back. The warm sunlight fell softly across my bed and a moment later, returned to consciousness, I was aware of the pleasantly featured young waitress who, having opened the curtains, moved across to me with the demeanour so charming that I broke out in English: 'Your country is truly the land of flowers!'

She blushed prettily and set the tray in front of me.

'You understand English then?' I exclaimed delightedly – the day before at table she had not uttered a word.

'Yes sir,' she said politely. 'Since we have so many English and American guests at the hotel, our manager insists that all the waitresses should speak a little English.'

I nodded delightedly. The Japanese were indeed a wonderful people!

'How old are you?' I asked.

'I am nearly nineteen!' she exclaimed.

'You are very pretty,' I said with a smile, hoping to draw her out. 'I'm sure all the young men must be in love with you!'

'Indeed no, sir!' she laughed, bowing her pretty head. Never once did she indicate that she desired to leave the room, not by gesture nor by expression. She was the essence of politeness. Of course my interest was aroused at once. I had had a good night's sleep and my first vision upon waking up was of this pretty girl with the sun shining on her pretty, neatly starched uniform.

'Tell me,' I said provokingly, 'is love forbidden in your country that a beautiful girl like you has not a hundred admirers?'

She laughed and then shook her head engagingly.

'Perhaps it's that you have no desire for love,' I went on. 'Perhaps the young men are afraid that you will reproach them!'

Still she would not speak, but her smile remained and a soft light flickered in her delicate almond-shaped eyes.

'Come,' I said, 'tell me the truth about yourself! Do you never long to have the experience of being loved? Has no man ever caressed you? Have you never given yourself completely to a man's embraces?'

'Oh, sir,' she said, 'why should you be interested in my poor life? I am a woman. That is all. There is no secret!'

'No secret?'

'What is there secret in a woman's desire?'

'And in her body?'

'It is a body, like any other. If there is any mystery it is in a woman's soul.'

'Will you prove it to me?'

'How?' Her dark eyes flickered softly and there was a smile on her delicate, poppy-red lips.

'By showing it to me of course!' I said with a smile.

'Oh sir,' she said gaily, 'you can see women any day in our country, in the public baths, and in the country districts, even on the streets!'

'That is all very well,' I said, 'but it is your body I want to see. Will you show it to me?'

She hesitated. I laughed. 'You see? And now I shall not believe a word you have said!'

Imagine my surprise when, without a word, she began to undress before me! A moment later she was standing, young, sinuous and radiant. Naked as the day she was born. Her body was perfect – the breasts small and round with light brown nipples no bigger than raisins, her thighs slim and full at the same time, and her buttocks firm and poised tremulously beneath her narrow waist.

I did not need to ask her to turn this way and that so that I might examine her more particularly; she appeared to realise intuitively that I wished to have a glimpse of her from all angles. Thus she posed for me, first facing me and then with her back toward me, and then suddenly she clasped her hands in front of me and laughed.

Without hesitation, I slipped from the bed and crossed the floor toward her. I too was naked, having thrown off my nightgown as I rose from the bed. She made no effort to flee away from me, but waited until I had traversed the distance between us and had placed my hands on her slim shoulders. 'How perfectly lovely you are! I exclaimed.

She laughed and swayed forward, touching her firm little breasts against my chest tantalisingly. I looked down between them and saw the neat, small, triangular shape of her mound with its smooth plumage of blue-black hair which threaded its way delicately upwards toward her navel. I encircled her with my arms and crushed her body close. She lay against me without resisting, one of her knees raised slightly against my thigh. I was utterly delighted with her. Was it *naïveté* that caused her to allow a stranger to clasp her close in this way?

I think that would be the wrong word. No, it was rather the true innocence of the pagan who is happily incapable of comprehending our Western notion of modesty. It seemed the most natural thing in the world to her to satisfy my curiosity. She rejoiced in the affirmation of her young sex, in the possibility of the carnal delight which, untroubled by the cataracts of morality, was a thing to be taken and held firmly while her youth was still with her.

Very gently, I reached round under her buttocks with one arm and raised her from the floor. She seemed to have no density at all. I carried her across to the bed without effort and laid her at full length on the warm sheets. She smiled up at me, still passive except for the falling sideways of one thigh which revealed between the smooth surfaces the delicate pink tract of her sex. Without haste, I leaned over her and took her left nipple between my lips. I sucked on it gently and felt her breast grow hard under my mouth. Her eyes flickered beneath their long, smooth lashes, and then, like delicate curtains, were closed. At the same time, she raised her knees and allowed them to fall open like loose scissors. This had the effect of distending her sex in such a way that the hair near its summit parted to reveal the little bud of her clitoris. I moved my fingers there gently to stimulate the flow of her love juice and at the first contact of my fingers her pretty mouth fell open to allow herself to be submerged in her passion. Soon I felt her body arch upwards in its effort to give itself completely and then her delicate little hands sought my head and guided it skilfully between her thighs so that my mouth came to rest on the smooth pad of hair which parted like grass under the gentle strokes of my tongue. The whole affair had been so casual, without hurry, without breathlessness, that I had perhaps more time to examine her sex than I had hitherto had in any previous experience of that kind. I was able to examine the way in which each individual hair was embedded in the pulpy flesh of her mound. The way in which they had a tendency to curl toward the tips, doubtless owing to the fact that she had habitually worn a kind of loincloth which not only compressed the hairs but caused a delicate and not at all pungent sweat to gather there. Her sex was exceedingly small, much smaller than any of the Chinese women with whom I had had sexual experiences during the past few months. Indeed, I don't think it would be an exaggeration to say that it was the smallest, and perhaps the prettiest, sex I had ever seen. Up till that moment, of course. I don't wish to give the impression this girl was in any way outstanding amongst her fellow countrymen. On the contrary, if I began by saying that the Japanese are the most passionate and tender of women, I might add now that their loins and their sexes are in general far more dainty than those of any other race.

Soon I allowed my tongue to move in between the sloping hair-trimmed surfaces. Her love juice was not at all unpleasant to taste and reminded me more than anything else of the white of an egg, but with a heavier, human quality about it, doubtless again because of the hothouse atmosphere which was the normal condition of her private parts. I stroked slowly, worrying the little stamen of her clitoris with my upper lip at the same time as I penetrated more deeply with my tongue. By this time her hands had come underneath her buttocks and she raised herself to the length of her forearms and supported herself on twin pedestals, her legs wide and astride like the shafts of a cart. How soft and satin-like were her thighs against my cheeks! When she allowed her buttocks to sink downwards, she groaned, bucked slightly, and then, taking me by the hair of my head, drew me upwards until my sex broke softly into hers and slid, warmly coated by the love juice, inward deeply to the hilt. At once I felt my sex and my short hairs inundated by the delicate froth of her loins. I sighed and undulated my hips gently in the motions of love.

'You darling!' I cried. 'You are making me all wet!

She answered me with a pretty smile, and then, her face growing serious, she drew my mouth down against her own. Her little tongue darted into my mouth and traced delicate filigrees behind my teeth. Our teeth clicked and we burst out laughing. I seized her thick hair which had been cut in the usual way in which Japanese women style it, that is to say, it is cut short of shoulder length and falls like a bell about the pronounced Oriental cheeks, and I pinned her laughing head to the bed.

'How pretty you are!' I couldn't help exclaiming, 'What a marvellous time we are going to have together while I am here!'

'Be more brutal,' she said softly, her rich voice tinged with insinuation, 'I want you to try to kill me by loving!'

In immediate response to her desire I thrust violently into her with strong strokes. Her belly grew wet with perspiration and her pretty mouth, the teeth bared, drove itself into my neck. I rose and fell on her, relishing the soft smacking sound which the thick, hollow flesh of our bellies created between them. She was mad with lust. She forgot her English words and a stream of Japanese words and exclamations burst from her lips against my neck and shoulders, her voice husky and lilting in a typically Oriental way. What enjoyment I derived from that slim body with its blue-black hair at sex and armpits!

As we rose to our first climax, exactly simultaneously, we both cried out in our native tongues and settled, our perspiration mingling and my seed carried upwards in the gentle alluvial flow which love caused to rise in her. Only then, only at that tremendous moment, did I remember that I had not asked her whether she had taken precautions against conception. I did so at once. She shook her head laughingly. But I was serious. I had no desire that the sweet child should become pregnant by me.

Thus, in spite of her expostulations, I withdrew, opened my suitcase which I had not yet had time to unpack and brought out my syringe. I explained how she should use it and would have nothing to do with her until she followed my instructions to the letter. Then, her small face puckered up in mock anger, she came into my arms again. Suddenly she emitted a long, tearful wail and dropped to her knees. One of her hands grasped my member and thrust it into her mouth. Gazing downwards at the pretty head which sought to bury itself at my groin, I was amazed to see that my own sex was once again rigid.

No sooner did the realisation come over me – like a minute bristle at all my pores – than I allowed myself to topple sideways on to the carpet on which, for the space of five minutes, we wrestled and fought uncontrolledly until, once again, her little belly rising upwards to expose her naked sex, I drove mine into her with all my might. She breathed deeply between her sobs and our passion caused our flesh to shudder more deeply than I can remember. By this time I had pinioned her hands to the floor on either side so that she lay as though crucified below me. I rose and fell against her, our bellies smacking together in a welter of sweat until, just as the new inundation coursed through the sensitive tissue of my flanks, I felt her body grow weak, accepting the ichor of my passion. Her lovely young face, tearful and ecstatic at the same time, pleaded with me to stop.

'Oh,' she cried. 'Stop now . . . I can't bear any more . . . I shall die of pleasure! Please . . . '

Her eyes were closed and her tremulous young bosom rose and fell out of all control. Her limbs were slack and spreadeagled on the floor. All possibility of effort had deserted her!

Gently, more tenderly than ever, I rose from her, lifted her lovely young torso in my arms and carried her to the bed. She was in no condition to take the necessary precautions herself and so I did the work with the syringe, for I would not for the world have brought the pain of an unwanted pregnancy to a young female who had given me so much pleasure. Ten minutes later she opened her eyes. The coffee which she had brought was only lukewarm but it seemed to revive her and she drank it gratefully from the cup which I held to her lips.

'You gave me so much love!' she said when she had drunk. 'Really, I thought my body would burst with pleasure.'

I kissed her gently and told her to rest for the remainder of the day. I would explain to the manager, I told her. She should have no fear of taking the rest she so well deserved and so badly needed. I kissed her, drew the bedclothes upwards over her lovely little shoulders and went about my own toilet with the feeling that I had found at last the country in which love, in all its varied beauty, is accepted gratefully without shame as the most important gift in a good life.

I was invited by my friend Captain B to a festive evening. He had brought together a special corps of geishas, and they were attended by *mousmées* who came and sat with us while their more exalted sisters danced. The little *mousmée* who came to me was the prettiest of the whole lot and I suppose I showed her that I admired her. At any rate, the dance was not half over when her hand began to stray and from light touches, the brushing of her fingers against my thigh, she soon went on to bolder demonstrations of desire. At length I said to her 'later', one of the few Japanese words I knew; she pouted and then laughed with enjoyment. I allowed my hand to move softly over the silk of her tunic. When the geishas finished their dance and came back to sit with us, I said to my host, 'Is it possible for me to keep the little *mousmée*?'

'Sure,' he replied, and with a word or two made my resolve known. Never did I see such gratitude in any human face as the little *mousmée* showed me there. I was sure that the compliment paid to her in preferring her to the more important geishas would be returned in full. I was not mistaken. As soon as we were alone together in the bedroom later that night, she evinced a mixture of affection and passion such as it has seldom been my good fortune to experience

I made the mistake of thinking that after the first night it was all over. When Captain B and I met in the morning, I told him all my feelings and gave him a ten-pound note to convey my satisfaction to my little friend. To my wonder and his, the money was refused! Captain B declared that it was the first time in all his twenty years acquaintance with Japan that such a thing had happened.

It was my little *mousmée* who taught me all I know of Japan and a good deal of female nature to boot. The moment we spoke of sex things her revelations became extraordinary. She told me never to go with anyone in the Yoshiwara: if I wanted anyone she would soon find out if they were healthy or not and let me know.

When I think of the devotion of that *mousmée* I am always astonished. She loved me, yet never showed any jealously; on one of the first occasions she brought a pretty geisha to me saying: 'She is famous but I don't think you'll care for her.' Then she got her to lie down and exposed her sex: 'You see,' she said, parting her lips, 'she's not very small and she takes a long time to excite.'

'How do you know that?' I asked.

'Because I tried before bothering you with her; but she wanted to come, thinking, I suppose, her eyes would win you.' And the girl's eyes were indeed very pretty. Barring exact detail, I think I have said enough to show the extent of my debt to my little *mousmée*. It remains only for me to describe one heavenly night which I spent in her company.

To be precise, there was another girl present, another *mousmée* whom she had selected carefully for our night of love 'Look!' she said when she produced this friend, 'she is really worth love! Her sex is smaller than mine and with one touch it is all aflame!'

As I stood gazing at these two adorable creatures, each one nude, each perfect in her own way, I felt a tremendous desire stir in my loins. 'And don't think I'm going to leave you alone with her!' my *mousmée* laughed merrily. 'Who knows? Both of us together may be able to keep you here in Kyoto! For I know you love me, Frank, and if what you say about your Western women is true I don't understand why you wish to return to them. And now, use us, dear! Just as you please!'

For a moment I was too dumbfounded to move! These two superb creatures with pale skin, their neat hips, their perfect breasts, and their almost identical heads set high on smooth, proud necks and capped by neat bells of blue-black hair – I had never before been offered so much and so delightfully! As I say, I was for a moment incapable of the slightest movement. But at last I said: 'Stand where you are, close together, facing me!'

They laughed prettily and did as they were bid. Quickly, I removed my own clothes so that I stood naked before them. My eyes were hypnotised by the twin sexes, by the neat chevrons of silky, dark hairs which clung close to their lower bellies and disappeared in a neat point at the junction of their thighs, and even more perhaps by the beautiful ivory smoothness of the bellies themselves, indented neatly at their centres by the prettiest of navels. I moved over to them and, falling on my knees in front of them, encircled the smooth buttocks of each with either arm. The choice was before me – two pretty sexes, delicately scented in a manner which only Japanese women know, at the level of my doting lips.

'Taste us in turn!' my own little *mousmée* laughed delightedly. 'Her first – she is the guest!'

With my forehead against the warm belly of the other little *mousmée*, I allowed my lips to mingle with her silky hairs, parting them with my tongue to find her sweet-smelling little clitoris.

Both girls were laughing prettily and talking in Japanese.

'What are you saying?' I said, faintly annoyed with their laughter

'Only that you will have to dig deep to find the gold!' exclaimed my own little friend in her sweet voice.

At that very moment my tongue, moving tentatively between the delicately fringed lips of the girl's sex, tasted an indescribable sweetness. I allowed my tongue to sink between the lips into the soft mass. Imagine my astonishment when a perfectly delightful ichor spread about my taste buds! The nearest I can come to the description of it is to say that it had the consistency of honey and tasted of violet and rose leaves. At the same time I was conscious of the girl's quiver under my caress.

'You darlings!' I cried, 'what have you done to yourselves?'

'An old love secret,' my little *mousmée* explained, and then she added, 'why don't you take us both over to the divan where we can be comfortable and relax. If my guess is correct you will want to explore us both in this way for a long time!'

How right she was! The divan was a broad one. I lay between them with my feet toward their heads, and my sex, rampant now with the urgency of the situation, on a level with their mouths. I tasted first one and then the other, exploring, suckling, savouring, while they, darling lovers that they were, moved about my loins with their soft mouths, teasing my body into ecstasy. Soon both sexes became sticky and wet under my mouth, four lovely thighs rose upwards to allow deeper and more intimate penetrations, and the coral lips of the young and small sexes opened like wet and loving mouths, much as flowers might, to exude the sweetest of ichors. If I had to say what liquid came nearest in my imagination to the mythical ambrosia, I would say that the liquid distilled in those warm, ruby sheaths, mingling with the potion they had secreted there to lure me on was undoubtedly the one. My lips were afire with lust to taste more deeply, more urgently, spreading the fairy love juice amongst the shining hairs and on to the soft, delicately female-scented thighs. How lovely those thighs were, loose and lascivious, falling, moving like the slow tentacles of an underwater plant. Simultaneously, my own loins were besieged by the gentlest aerial attack of butterflies. I was lying on my side, first on one side and then on the other, to taste of two equally exotic honeycombs, with one maiden taking my member between her wet and cushioned lips and then the other.

Indeed, I quite forgot which was which, so I had no opportunity of showing preference!

That was the beginning. As my tonguing became more purposeful, my upper lip working the clitoris as my tongue delved deep among the ambrosia, each in her turn rose to a frantic climax, the torso quivering in rapture, the twin sighs, of the one who doted moaning with husky softness to incite, and the one who experienced the orgasm crying out fitfully as the seed rose in her womb, and I, my hands close at her bare buttocks, drawing the warm, sweet mass, as though to suffocate, about my face.

In this way, over a period of an hour, I raised them each three times to the highest pitch of experience, and found, much to my dismay – I myself had discharged twice under their twin caress, my seed swallowed lovingly by the girls in turn – that they were only eager for more, only eager to make a perpetual night of this almost religious adoration!

~ 2 ~

Immortalia

EDITED BY T. R. SMITH, 1927

The most sophisticated volume of adult verse ever collected and published in the United States is without doubt *Immortalia*. This legendary tome first appeared in 1927, a privately printed book, limited to a thousand copies for subscribers only, none otherwise for sale. It proclaimed itself 'an anthology of American ballads, sailors' songs, cowboy songs, college songs, parodies, limericks, and other humorous verses and doggerel, now for the first time brought together in book form by a Gentleman About Town'. The title said it all, except that the 'Gentleman' responsible was T. R. Smith (the famed editor for the publishing house of Boni & Liveright), the publisher was Macy–Masius (later famous for finely printed Limited-Editions Club books), and the place of publication was New York City.

Immortalia was a literary accident, an afterthought just too good to pass up. In the mid-1910s, T. R. Smith started the largest editing endeavour of his career. He wished to amass and publish the greatest American anthology of 'amatory verse'. He therefore gathered examples of poetry where 'Eros rules and Aphrodite guides' from all times in history, and from all over the world. The result, *Poetica Erotica*, appeared in 1921 in three volumes totalling nearly one thousand pages! Though a limited-edition publication, it specifically excluded works that were 'coarse, obscene, or vulgarly offensive'.

So massive a collection of verse was not unique to Smith. Over the centuries there had been many such compilations, some published for sale, and others kept as manuscript collections for mainly academic purposes. In England alone there had been *Pills to Purge Melancholy*, *The Roxburghe Ballads*, *Bishop Percy's Folio*, *The Musical Miscellany* and the various *Drollery* collections of the seventeenth century. The largest by far, though, being five volumes of nearly fifteen hundred pages, was

J. S. Farmer's *National Ballad and Song: Merry Songs and Ballads Prior to the Year AD 1800*, published in 1895–7, to which was added a sixth volume of 'canting songs and slang rhyme' that was over 250 pages. All these early anthologies contained songs and folk ballads that dealt with various aspects of love and amorous activity. Some of the collections even contained examples that were *risqué*, scatological, or downright obscene. (Farmer in fact sought out erotic and explicit material, and went so far as to reprint Robert Burns's banned and suppressed *Merry Muses of Caledonia*.)

Why then do another anthology? T. R. Smith was familiar with all these collections, and saw that they were next to impossible for his American readers to penetrate. The 'olde Englysh' spellings and sentence structures left them solely in the realm of scholars and academics. Also, they for the most part ignored the erotic verse of established poets (such as the Restoration *carpe-diem* school) who were openly published during their own lifetimes in volumes that had become exceedingly rare in any edition. Perhaps most important, Smith was particularly interested in 'modern' (i.e. post 1900) poetry. To that latter end he solicited material from his many literary friends and colleagues. Like his predecessors, he, too, collected a number of works (mainly sexual parodies of well-known pieces) that while excellently written (frequently by very well-known and respected poets) simply could not be included in even a limited-edition work issued only for a mature audience. The pieces though were just too good not to print.

This editorial predicament was not without precedent. In 1867 the editors of *Bishop Percy's Folio* found a number of items in the manuscript collection of folk ballads and songs simply too dirty to print openly. Being, however, academics first and editors second, they elected to issue the erotic pieces separately as a very limited, restricted supplement to the main volumes. T. R. Smith elected to do the same, and hence *Immortalia* came to be created from the 'vulgar' left-over scraps of *Poetica Erotica*.

Smith knew exactly what he was doing, as he clearly states in *Immortalia*'s introduction:

> The Gentleman About Town has performed a service of notable worth in preserving and giving definitive form to the wealth of latter-day folklore which is contained within the covers of *Immortalia*. American folklore has of necessity sought cover, driven by the indiscriminating tirades and sadistic tyrannies of the Mrs Grundys who are an irremovable part of this *mélange* we know as modern civilisation . . . It is not the purpose of this book to override good

A Toast

ANONYMOUS

A social glass
And a social lass
Go very well together.
But a social lass
With a social ass
I think a damn sight better.
Here's to the glass,
And the lass, and the ass,
May we meet in all kinds of weather;
We'll drink from the glass,
And feel of the ass,
And make the lass feel better.

Strip Poker

ANONYMOUS

Betty and Billy, myself and fair Milly,
Once sat in a strip-poker game.
All of us truly were young and unruly,
But the pep it was there just the same.

The cards that I had were running quite bad,
Then suddenly, they came to me great:
From out of the slush, I cornered a flush
Of diamonds, the four to the eight.

Betty and Billy dropped out, leaving Milly
And yours very truly to fight it alone:
I raised it a tie and, flicker me eye,
She saw it and raised it a comb.

This kinda hurt, I saw with my shirt,
With a coat I raised in great haste.
She looked with her belt and, 'Oi gevelt!'
Boosted it high with her waist.

But I didn't flinch, it sure was a cinch,
So I bet every stitch that I had.
She saw, if you please, with her silken chemise
And – [stopped by the censors] – too bad!

The Ship's in the Harbour

ANONYMOUS

Oh, the ship's in the harbour,
She lies by the dock,
Like a young girl and a young man
With a stiff standing

– haul away for the mainsail,
The main-top-set-sail,
Haul away for the mainsail,
The main-top-set-sail.

And there was young Johnny,
The pride of her crew,
Who liked to drink whisky
And also to

– water the garden when
He was at home,
Water the garden when
He was at home.

He could dive like a diver,
He could swim like a duck,
He could show the young ladies
A new way to

– save their sweet lives if
A cramp they should take,
Save their sweet lives if
A cramp they should take.

But alas, we put it in at
A far Northern port,
And he froze it in chasing
And broke it off

– halfway to Juneau,
And halfway to Nome,
Halfway to Juneau,
And halfway to Nome.

Oh, the ship's in the harbour,
She lies by the dock,
But alas for poor Johnny,
He has no more

– yardarm to splice with,
Or topmast to brace,
Yardarm to splice with,
Or topmast to brace.

Berkeley

ANONYMOUS

O, Harvard is run by Princeton,
And Princeton is run by Yale,
And Yale is run by Vassar,
And Vassar's run by tail;
But Stanford's run by stud-horse juice,
They say its made by hand,
It's the house of clap and syph,
It's the asshole of the land.

The Yougest Child

ANONYMOUS

She lay stark naked
Between the sheets,
So nice and fat and chubby;
And I myself beside her lay,
My hand upon her bubby.
I kissed her lips in crazy glee,
And 'neath her chin did chuck her:
Our thighs did intermingle,
And I began to fuck her.
'Pull out,' she cried, 'pull out! pull out,
Or I'll get me into trouble.'
I did, and on her snow-white breast
That stream did squirt and bubble.
I looked into her frightened face
And, with a smile of mirth,
I said, 'I guess that is the youngest child
That you have ever nursed.'
She scooped it up with one fair hand,
And, with a glad ha ha,
She threw the load into my face
And said, 'Child, go kiss your pa!'

Your Radiator's Bursted

ANONYMOUS

Your radiator's bursted,
And your dust-pan's on the bum;
Your gearshift's dry and rusted,
And you cannot go or come.

Your four-wheel brakes have lost their grip
As anyone can tell –
Your clutch is loose and bound to slip;
Your rear-end's shot to hell.

Your spark-plugs fail to get the juice,
Your lights are on the bum.
Your rear-wheel lugs are mighty loose,
You've sure been going some.

Your windshield's broke, your starter's stuck,
Your rear-end lights won't burn;
In fact, old top, you're out of luck
And hardly worth a durn.

I'll get the parts I know you need:
Some monkey glands and such,
But you must cut down on your speed,
And not go out so much;

For your rambling days, old top,
Are over now, and past.
It's not because you ran the race,
It's 'cause you ran too fast!

There was an Old Man

ANONYMOUS

There was an old man sitting on a rock,
Watching little boys playing with their –
Agates and marbles in Springtime of yore;
While over in the bushes they watched a fat –
Brunette young lady sitting in the grass;
When she rolled over you could see her shapely –
Shoes and stockings that fit like a duck;
She said she was learning a new way to –
Bring up her children and teach them to knit;
As over in the bushes they were taking a –
Little companion down to the docks;
And said they would show him the length of their –
You may think this is bullshit,
But it isn't, by God!

Why Dogs Leave a Nice Fat Bone

ANONYMOUS

The dogs once held a meeting
They came from near and far;
Some came in automobiles,
Some came in a car.

But before inside the hall
They were allowed to take a look,
They had to take their assholes off,
And hang them on a hook.

They all walked in, one by one,
Mother, son and sire,
But no sooner were they seated
Than someone hollered, 'Fire!'

Then they all rushed out in a bunch,
They had no time to look;
So each one grabbed an asshole
And ran it off the hook.

They got their assholes all mixed up,
It made them awfully sore
To think they'd lost the asshole
They'd always worn before.

And that's the reason why
When you go down the street,
A dog will stop and swap a smell
With every dog he meets.

And that's the reason why
A dog will leave a nice fat bone,
To smell another's asshole,
In hopes to find his own.

The Mortal

ANONYMOUS

Once upon a midnight dreary
When of smoking I was weary,
And had drunk up all my whisky
Only wishing there was more;
Suddenly there came a rapping
As of some fair female tapping,
Tapping at my chamber door.
'Tis some chippy that's a-wishin'
To my room to gain admission.
Well, I'll rise and let her enter,
Enter though she be a whore,
Only that, and nothing more.

So I opened wide the portal,
And there stood such a mortal
As in all my living moments,
I had never seen before.
She had lost her upper garments,
And of all seductive varmints,
She was sure the warmest baby
Mortal woman ever bore;
And each palpitating bubby
Was so round and firm and chubby,
That my spirits rose within me,
Just my spirits, nothing more.

'Twas the fourteenth of December;
But more clearly I remember
When I woke up in the morning
Of December twenty-four –
Sequel of ten days before.

All that's left of what passed between us
Is one poor infected penis;
Drooping, red and retrospective,
Penitent, and very sore;

And that penis still is dripping,
Still is dripping, dripping, dripping,
Every morning, every evening,
Dripping on the bathroom floor.
And I murmur vows forgotten
Every time I change the cotton.
No more tapping, no more rapping,
No, never, nevermore.

Whang

ANONYMOUS

I'll tell you a little story,
Just a story I have heard,
And you'll swear it's all a fable
But it's gospel every word.

When the Lord made father Adam
They say he laughed and sang,
And sewed him up the belly
With a little piece of whang.

But when the Lord was finished
He found he'd measured wrong;
For when the whang was knotted
'Twas several inches long.

Said he, ' 'Tis but eight inches
So I guess I'll let it hang.'
So he left on Adam's belly
That little piece of whang.

But when the Lord made mother Eve
I imagine he did snort,
When he found the whang he sewed
Her with was inches short.

' 'Twill leave an awful gap,' said he,
'But I should give a damn,
She can fight it out with Adam
For that little piece of whang.'

So ever since that day
When Human life began,
There's been a constant struggle
'Twixt the woman and the man.

Women swear they'll have the piece
That from our belly hangs,
To fill the awful crack left when
The Lord ran out of whang.

So let us not be jealous boys,
With that which women lack,
But lend that little piece of whang
To fill that awful crack.

Mary's Little Lamb

ANONYMOUS

Mary had a little lamb,
Its fleece was white as snow;
And everywhere that Mary went
The lamb was sure to go.

It followed her to the barn one day
For eggs she was to hunt;
It stuck its nose beneath her clothes
To get a whiff of cunt.

Now, Mary was a naughty girl
And didn't give a damn;
She let him have another whiff
And killed the god-damned lamb.

Limericks

There was an old lady from Grott,
Who lived on green apples and snot;
When she couldn't get these,
She lived on the cheese
She scraped from the end of her twat.

There was an old man from Nantucket,
Whose cock was so long he could suck it;
He said with a grin,
As he wiped off his chin,
'If my ear was a cunt I could fuck it.'

I love her in the evening gown,
I love her in her nightie;
But when moonlight flits
Between her tits,
Jesus Christ, almighty!

There was a young man from Kent
Whose prick was so long it bent,
To save himself trouble
He put it in double,
And instead of coming he went.

There was a young lady from Lichen
Was scratching her cunt in the kitchen;
Her mother said, 'Rose,
It's crabs I suppose' –
'Yes, and by Jesus, they're itchin'.'

There was a young girl from Anhuyser
Who said that no man could surprise her,
But Pabst took a chance,
Found Schlitz in her pants,
And now she is sadder Budweiser.

There was a young man of Bombay,
Who moulded a cunt out of clay,
 But the heat of his prick
Turned the clay into brick,
And wore all his foreskin away.

There was a young lady from Clyde,
Who'd no ticket on which to ride,
So she told the conductor
Who immediately fucked her,
And gave her two dollars beside.

There was a young man from Montrose
Who screwed himself with his toes:
He could do it so neat
He fell in love with his feet,
And christened them Myrtle and Rose.

There was a man from Montclair
Who was screwing his girl on a chair;
At the twenty-first stroke
The little chair broke,
And his gun went off in the air.

3

The Erotic Professor

*c.*1930

The anonymously authored *The Erotic Professor* was written in the early 1930s. The novel is clearly American based on the language, style and plot, although it proclaims itself to be set in England. The professor of the title, Joseph Babcock, finds it necessary to prostitute his lovely and much younger wife Doris in a very special way to retain his university tenure and keep his academic position secure and his finances solvent. The old codgers who control the professor's future are inveterate voyeurs, and have picked Babcock to provide the sexual situations to be spied on, to satisfy their perverted lusts.

It is an ironic twist of fate that brings the student Clive Murray (the narrator of this tale) into the arms and bed of the seemingly unobtainable woman he longs for, the delicious Mrs Babcock. Needing a good-looking stud to complete the erotic tableaux he has planned for his blackmailers, the professor sets up his wife with Clive, and has her tease him and seduce the young man, while making him think that her motivation is a simple matter of spousal revenge. The student is slowly lead into increasingly more exciting erotic situations, not knowing that he is being secretly watched.

The title of this book is perhaps inappropriate and misleading. The professor is in fact a minor character. His motivations of greed and professional security, at the expense of his honour, are obvious. It is the burgeoning sexuality of Clive Murray and the passionate willingness of the wife to participate in this charade that provide the novel's dynamic tension. If anything is being said about the psychology of sexuality in the early Depression years, it is said through these two characters. Whether this tale gives a false or eternally accurate portrayal of sexual blackmail in Academia is perhaps best left to the readers and their own personal experiences.

from *The Erotic Professor*

Poor Doris was in a state – a state in which she made no attempt now to conceal the fact that she longed for me to go in with her and to remove her futile garments and assuage her burning desires in whatever manner I wished.

It was clear that her rampageous bout with the happy and fortunate Steve, while soothing her for the time being, had resulted in simply stirring up the savage and marvellous passions of the velvet-bodied and damask-cheeked Doris until now she could make hardly a pretence of self-control.

Hovering about the open door of the dining room, she beckoned to me – hardly seeking to conceal her gesture from her quivering spouse or from the satiated, happy Stephen. As I simply smiled amiably at her, she stamped a bare foot softly – and she said: 'I would like to talk with you in private, Clive, about these garments. I'm certain we can be excused for just a minute – '

I arose then. My eyes narrowed. Doris blushed as I drew near to her.

I guided her through the opening and drew the doors together behind us. Flushing more deeply as I faced her, the brunette lady looked down.

'You – you do want to make love, don't you, darling?' she whispered nervously. 'Just because Steve and I – '

'But need you have satisfied him quite so well?' I asked, quite consternated myself. And I reached under her left arm – laying aside from her glorious bottom the gauzes that lay vaporously upon the mounds.

'Clive – beloved – what are you g–going to do?' she gasped.

'Behave yourself!' I told her.

'Are you going to undress me and – and – oh, my love – '

'Please do keep on for a minute what you are wearing!'

'Listen, dearest. Clive, darling, let me at least – kiss you!'

Dropping to her knees, she sent trembling hands to my buttons. Her teeth chattered as she inserted fingers which found and grasped my naked, rigid prick. Almost before I could take action in the matter, she had exposed my genitals totally.

'You're crazy, Doris!' I muttered.

'Perhaps, just now, I am,' she quavered. 'Yes, when I am alone with you, I believe I am unbalanced –'

Tenderly holding and caressing my prick, she was kissing it hotly.

'Control yourself – or you'll make me lose all my own self-control!' I said huskily.

'You do love my pettings, then, darling. Ah, you do enjoy them?'

'I love being inside your body whenever possible,' I muttered.

'My love, let's now – !'

'No, for there are other things to be done.'

'Oh sweetheart, how wicked. Do let me just suck your lovely prick for a moment!'

And to this, my passions rather than my will taking charge, I could offer no objection. She sucked me divinely, vibrating visibly in every nerve and muscle.

'Stop – sweetness – !' I warned her hoarsely.

All my fugitive animosity towards her, ensuing upon my discovery of her betrayal of our most intimate moments on the day preceding, had vanished. For how could one fail to forgive this creature of sheer passion and flame and beauty?

Yet she was not satisfied.

'Stop!' I commanded more firmly.

As she withdrew her rosy, congested lips, she raised dying eyes to my face.

'It's so w–wonderful!' she whispered.

'I should have spent in another instant,' I told her.

'And I – I should have swallowed every drop!' she breathed. 'Oh, let me, Clive!' I patted the small hands which reached eagerly for my prick again. I rebuttoned my nether garments after tucking away the focal object of her temptation.

'I am going into the other room – where two men are already wondering what we are doing,' I said.

'And I shall get into my clothes, Clive,' Doris said somberly. 'And I shall be for a while the seemingly respectable hostess – and the madness of this past hour will be ignored!'

'You will get into your clothes, yes – but not here. I want you to bring your apparel into the living room – and we shall see how your husband endures seeing you get out of these new fineries under three pairs of eyes.'

I then went into the other room. The eyes of Professor Babcock were dim and questioning as he gazed at me. Steve gave me a covert smile.

Doris followed me presently, carrying her discarded attire and still arrayed in my gift, the opaque, whimsical panties.

'I – I thought none of you would mind,' she said bashfully, 'if I changed in here, since we are all on such close and friendly terms. And truly, I was lonesome there in the dining room.'

Already she was loosening the shoulder straps of the fragile chemise. Down slipped the garment to her navel, revealing the glories of her twin breasts and all the beauties of her torso.

'You – you!' stammered her husband. 'You are a – !'

His voice trailed off into a gasp as I looked at him ominously and coldly.

'I am a what, dear?' she enquired cheerfully.

'A wonder! He was about to call you a marvel,' I interpreted. 'Weren't you, Prof?'

'Yes, a gem of lovely flesh,' he said.

Arrayed in just the airy, beribboned panties, Doris clasped her young breasts concealingly – as if suddenly bashful.

'I – I'm wondering,' she breathed, 'whether I am not doing a foolish thing – taking risks – in doing this. Really, I hardly dare take off the drawers.'

'And why not?' I asked.

'Well, you all pretend not to mind – not to think of naughty things. And I'm sure you and Steve have only pure thoughts regarding my sisterly audacity. But Joseph there – his eyes make me nervous.'

With a glance I admired her ingenious, accusing way of tugging her spouse into the situation in a sensual manner. I grinned at the flushed man – and I saw that there was more than jest behind the whimsical complaint of the brunette. For under all the consternation with which he had undergone his nerve-racking experience, there was revealed now a genuine, personal lust for the lovely lady with whom he had had no normal sexual relations, as she had told me, for some years.

'Oh, the Doc wouldn't do anything to mortify you,' I said.

He paid no attention. If there was humiliation and helpless wrath in his gaze, there were also the glowing eyes and the white teeth showing beneath a curling lip that betrayed his vast and intimate agitation.

'Hand me your drawers, Doris,' I said. 'I want to see whether they are as well made as I was told when I got them.'

Bending, she slowly slipped off the frothy garment. There appeared in view the small, dusky fleece of her cunt – the divine belly – all the wonderful, naked symmetry of the girl.

'There. Now I hope you are all satisfied!' she pouted as she came to deliver the panties into my extended hand.

This young woman, gloriously passionate, could not be naked in the presence of a man without visibly flaring. I fully believe that even if the man had been eighty years old and bedridden, her excitement would still have been manifest. And she stood there for a moment, trembling under three pairs of inflamed eyes, before bending to pick up the scant but opaque combination she had previously worn.

'Just an instant, Doris,' I remarked.

An infernal idea had come into my head, an idea for making this day additionally memorable for Professor Babcock by what I hoped would prove a wholesome torment.

'Your husband and I,' I said, 'heard suspicious sounds while you were in the dining room with Steve – sounds that annoyed us very much, as of two young human animals in heat and assuaging their desires.'

'For shame, Clive!' she exclaimed. 'As if we would do anything like that! You can just ask Steve if we weren't as nice as could be.'

'Didn't do a thing,' averred her new lover, 'except to try on her silly lingerie.'

'That's all,' repeated Doris indignantly. 'I hope we wouldn't forget what is due my husband and our friends so far as to –'

And then she gazed from me to her spouse.

'Why do you both look at me so accusingly?' she quavered. 'Great goodness, all that happened was that I undressed and let Steve see me in my lovely new underclothing. And I wouldn't have done that if Joseph hadn't insisted!'

Her husband shook his massive head as if trying to clear his brain of cobwebs. He said nothing, but his sensual excitement remained clear as he stared at his totally nude wife and beheld the manner in which other male desire converged upon her.

'Then what,' I enquired severely, 'were all those sighs and gasps that we heard – and all this business about "darling, give me every inch" and that wail of "I'm coming"?'

The nude lady had the grace to turn red – even though entering into this new plot of mine, which she couldn't yet quite fathom.

'We just decided to plague you and Joseph,' she said sweetly, 'by making it sound as if we were really being wicked together.'

'The Prof and I figured it out that way,' I said. 'We thought you were just trying something like that, didn't we, Doc?'

The beleaguered professor ground his teeth and muttered something inaudible.

'Your husband doesn't seem entirely convinced even yet,' I remarked. 'Fortunately, it's easy to tell whether you really let Steve get into your cunt.'

I steered the ravishing lady by a wrist to my chair. With no caressing preliminaries whatever, I lowered a hand to her fluffy beard, to her lightly opened cunt. I curved a finger inward.

Doris stiffened and gasped. She cast upon me a look of passion. She cast her head backward and her face upward. I knew, even without her sighs and the warm clinging of her throbbing passage to my finger, the frenzy I was causing her.

'I guess they're telling us the truth, Prof,' I said presently. 'It doesn't feel to me as if there's been anything in here recently. But you might see if you agree with me.

I pushed the tottering Doris towards the older man as I extracted my finger from her body. With a glance of torrid comprehension at me, she succumbed to what I so obviously wished.

She bent and rubbed her husband's brow with her tender breasts.

'Surely you're not going to be as suspicious of me, dear, as that horrid Clive,' she murmured. 'Perhaps – we could retire to the bedroom, dear.'

His teeth grated audibly once again. His chest was heaving.

Then all his feigned composure vanished – vanished in a whirlwind that astounded the vibrating Doris and startled us who looked on.

He drew the naked Doris to his lap. After a brief and instinctive withdrawal, she succumbed. Mutely her glance reminded me that I had wished this – that it was not she who would have submitted herself thus to her perverse husband, he who seemed miraculously to have normal desires for her after so long an interval. She drew her breath hissingly between her clenched even white teeth as he slowly drove a middle finger between the borders of her sexual groove.

'Oh – oh – oooh, Joseph!' she gasped. 'Think of what you are d–doing – and with our friends looking on!'

Professor Babcock replied only with breathing so stentorious that it was as a series of gasps. The nudity of his lovely wife, formerly a plaything for others, had caused by this time an agitation so intense that it amounted to a sensual madness.

With a middle finger buried within his writhing spouse, he bent his head to lay kissing, sucking lips to the glowing flower of one of her breasts. He raised his face presently and seemingly paid no attention to the panting expostulations of the twisting lady, who, held lightly by one of his arms, was startled yet fired by comprehending herself the target of a husbandly lust that she had supposed extinct forever. Steve and I eagerly awaited its outcome – the man stared vacantly with glazed eyes at my chum and myself, as if seeing us only as lecherous shadows that egged him on.

Suddenly, as Doris – perhaps averse to yielding herself to her husband as she had yielded herself, at my instigation, to Stephen Talley, yet so inflammable that every nerve in her beautiful body responded to this stimulation – clamoured and quivered with passion as her naked bottom rolled on his stiff and swollen prick and crazed him further, the man uttered a cry that was hardly human. It was more that of a rutting wolf than of an amorous human male. And he, too, began to pant out hoarsely a mass of tumbling words that confessed his awakened desires and that showered Doris, too, with praises for her erotic talents entirely deserved, for he himself was responsible for the lascivious tempest that had been brought upon her.

And this time I did not interfere nor did my friend. It was a *combat à deux – et à outrance*. Harsh, husky words flew back and forth between this amazing pair. For a moment the tormented man, though wild with all the emotions that had so long shaken him, averted his reddened face. But the veins stood out on his temples and his sexual congestion was visible. It was plain that not even all the outrages to which his husbandly prestige had been submitted could prevent him from lusting for his brunette wife. And he burned now in a way that gave the lie to the theory of Doris that his former physical desires for her body would never again boldly assert themselves.

And she knew what I was after now, the sweet imp! Perhaps her backward glance held regret that this added episode – for she felt it a far greater adventure to have to appear amorous of her spouse than to undergo what she had already permitted – should be added to her experiences of the evening.

'You – you know you just can't any more, Joseph.'

'Who the hell says I can't? I was never stiffer in my entire life. By God, I'm just as . . . Are you going to get down there on the floor?'

'Yes, Joseph. I am!'

'And lie there until I'm ready?'

'I will, dear – oh heavens! – but how unreasonable you are!'

He slipped her from his knees to the rug. Already tearing at his opened breeches, he turned to the corner for his preparations. His face was red and he shivered with lust. To our observant eyes it was apparent that his nerves had succumbed to the prolonged strain – that all the stimulation to which he had been submitted, the thrill of being able to look on and listen, had inflamed him greatly. There was no turning back now.

I went silently to tuck beneath her buttocks a cushion from the chair in which I had been sitting. Flat on her back and removing her hands from her flushed face, she gave me a pouting, perverse little moue, for her spouse was just then returning from the corner where he had left his clothing – all his clothing. He showed a well-preserved body. Though he saw me bending above the nude Doris and then retreating to my chair as he came towards her, he paid me no attention. His knees shook as, prying her legs apart, he knelt between them.

With eyes of flame he studied the delicate, faintly pink cleft of her most secret flesh. Tiny and girlish in appearance, it was truly worthy of the agitated appreciation of any man, sensualist or otherwise. Definitively separated from the small, silken, ebony fleece, which did not even curl down to its lips, it seemed set apart in its rose and white seclusion for an eternal state of maidenly chastity.

'God!' whispered the kneeling man huskily. 'God in heaven!'

Doris lay now in what seemed resignation to the inevitable. Yet, to me who had studied that lovely lady with some care, the quivering tension of all her superb nudity and the visible pulsation in the white throat beneath the hands that covered her face, told how strained was the leash that prevented her from wailing aloud her infinite passion and demanding an instant gratification from the man who crouched worshipfully above the exposed altar of her sex – even though that man had never spoken deeply to her senses and even though she thought him an unworthy substitute for the lover, or lovers, he had encouraged her to take.

'Why the hell doesn't the man get busy!' said Steve in a husky whisper.

'Be still!' I responded impatiently. 'Be quiet, and you may see something unexpected.'

Furtively the scientist spared us a glance. There was true rage at our presence in that glance, and the fury of feeling himself hampered by that presence. Then his fiery gaze settled once more on the tempting cunt of his young wife.

'For Christ's sake,' raved Steve almost silently. 'How long will it take the ass to get started! By now he ought to be into her to the roots!'

'Hush, you damned fool!' I muttered. 'Let him forget about us if he can. He's wrestling like hell with a temptation that you know nothing about. Yet, gross though he is, he's ashamed to give way to it while he is watched.'

Through parted fingers, Doris showed a dark eye that revealed that she had interpreted her husband's delay exactly as I had done. And this interpretation sufficed, I suppose, to keep her lying there patiently and fully exposed.

She had told me, you know, of the effect on her spouse and his desire to see her caressed by a young girl, Pearl. He had been aroused to emulate the latter – and it was my fancy that the delights he had felt in viewing this oral ministry to the passions of Doris had marked him forever with this sombre yearning.

He continued, nevertheless, to hesitate about showing himself a convert to this somewhat novel method of worshipping a womanly body under the eyes of us who gazed at him. The girl herself, pagan by nature and by instinct, would hardly at all mind having her two lovers see her husband thus ministering to her bliss – of this I felt confident.

Doctor Babcock was groaning softly. With a finger he touched the wee black beard – and then the pink furrow below. There was a dazed longing in the reddened face that he briefly showed us again.

And suddenly, gripping the soft thighs of his wife with both his hands, he lowered his face.

'Almighty God!' panted Steve in my ear. 'He – by God – he's kissing her cunny!'

'Wait – just wait – if you want to see a woman go perfectly insane!' I murmured.

'Forty devils,' rasped my chum. 'I've heard of such things – never saw them done. God, man – he's licking her beard – her pussy – and there goes his tongue right on her slit!'

The professor had been well-advised, it seemed, in clutching Doris's superb legs before settling his mouth and tongue on her sex. For no sooner did she feel that licking, lecherous caress than she bounced on her buttocks and, with hoarse little wails that were almost squeals of frenzied delight, she twisted and writhed in an involuntary tempest that would have dislodged his mouth if he had not maintained his grip upon her soft flesh.

Her cries ceased. Only her hoarse breathing broke the silence. She had removed her hands from her face. She had cast her arms to either side of her body – a body that shuddered and seemed convulsed with rising rapture. Her lovely face was a mask of ecstasy.

'Listen. By God, he's putting his tongue inside her!' said Steve. 'How the hell do you suppose he got started at this?'

'Be still. He saw a girl sucking her – and that seemed to set him afire. He hadn't fucked her for years, but he's done this several times since . . . '

'Joseph. O-o-oh, Joseph!'

It was this prolonged wail from Doris that checked our muttered conversation.

And now we saw something upon which neither of us had calculated. For, as Mrs Babcock arched her nether parts under the influence of sensations that racked her, all her expanded crotch became visible. And, groaning with a sombre delight, the man withdrew his tongue from the spot where he had thrust it and began to kiss her rosy clitoris with a burning and evident joy that made him forgetful now that they were not alone.

'Ahh . . . ahh . . . ahhh-ha!' quavered the young woman.

And, as his lips dwelt on her button of love, she flailed the floor with her arms and twisted her head from side to side. Her toes chanced to touch the rigid column of her husband's virility, and she jumped as if from an electrical shock.

'Joseph, Joseph! Now! Now!' she clamoured thickly. The vibrating man comprehended. Raging with the lust that made him at least temporarily virile, he shifted his body to board the brunette lady in normal fashion. And – multiplied into madness by all the lecheries that had preceded the consummation – Steve and I saw at last the ecstatic and natural communion of these amazing spouses.

Three minutes after their mutual explosions, Doctor Babcock – now realising fully all that had occurred and refraining from looking at any of us – was sheepishly donning his clothes in the corner. His wife still lay where she had been placed, looking up at Steve and myself dreamily, but with a dawning mischief in her face as she saw our expressions and noted the silent shame of her husband.

'I hope you two are satisfied, having seen what you wanted!' she observed. 'But I must say I am pleasantly surprised at my husband – putting his prowess on display like that!'

'Just a bit of fun with the boys here,' mumbled the man unsteadily. 'Hee-hee, it's fun to fuck you under any conditions my love. Hee-hee-hee.'

~ 4 ~

Grushenka

VAL LEWTON 1933

Grushenka, or Three Times a Woman first appeared in 1933. There was initial confusion as to whether the book was truly a translation of a nineteenth-century Russian novel, as it claimed to be in its preface and forward (by the mysterious translator 'J. D.'). There seemed to be inconsistencies and anachronisms in the text, although no one argued that it was not one of the best written erotic books they had ever come across, and obviously the work of a real professional writer. The truth of the matter is that Grushenka is an original American erotic novel, authored by Val Lewton, the Hollywood scriptwriter perhaps best remembered for his work on the original cinema version of *The Cat People*.

In summary, *Grushenka* is a *Fanny Hill* type story set in brutal Imperial Russia at the beginning of the eighteenth century. It recounts the history and sufferings of the protagonist, from her beginnings as a poor serf girl through to her ultimate success as the madame of a famous brothel. Her rise was through the sexual *sub rosa* of Russian society, and her story is a series of lascivious adventures told explicitly in a masterfully literate style.

Those seeking sexual verisimilitude, such as the accurate contemporary descriptions to be found in Cleland's *Fanny Hill* or Sellon's *The Ups and Downs of Life*, will be disappointed. Those seeking a lusty novel worthy of Czarist Russia will be amply rewarded.

from *Grushenka*

The droshky driver, warmed by a drink from a nearby public house. saluted Katerina, the old housekeeper, cheerfully and coaxed her to hire him again. He hoped that Her Eminence had completed her mission perfectly and that he could drive her home at roaring speed. Katerina let him know that she had been unsuccessful and that she would have to give up. Then the befuddled driver remembered that she wanted to hire some girls, and anew praised the goods which his cousin wanted to be rid of. He'd drive her over quickly and –

Katerina looked at the sun. It was still early. She climbed into the carriage, which answered with a sigh, bending to her weight.

We soon see Katerina heavily breathing while climbing up a creaking and steep staircase to the cousin's attic. It turned out that this cousin, a thin spinster of about fifty years, was handling an embroidery business on a small scale; that she had two girls working for her; and that she wanted to give up her enterprise and leave Moscow in order to stay with relatives in the south. Lacking money for the long trip, the fee from the girls' new employer should provide the means. Katerina was led into the adjoining room, a large, very light attic room, bare of any furniture except a worktable crowded with materials of all kinds.

On a bench before this table, bent over their work, sat two girls. The cousin commanded them to rise and it was then that Katerina uttered a cry of amazement. One of the girls was an exact duplicate of her princess; at least her face and features were so perfectly like those of her mistress that Katerina first feared a spook might have tricked her. Still, the face did not matter at all. It was only the right contours of the body which were sought. The height was right, the form seemed so, and Katerina hastily demanded that this dark-haired girl with the shining blue eyes be stripped. The other girl was a short, flat-nosed. sturdy creature and Katerina disregarded her. Not so the cousin. She made it quite clear that she would not part with one girl alone; it must be both or neither. Katerina mumbled that all that could be arranged; just let her see the dark one.

The girls flushed slightly, looked at each other and at the cousin, and stood sheepishly. The cousin demanded to know whether the dark girl had become deaf and when she wanted to take her clothes off. With excited fingers, the buttons of the blouse opened; then came a bodice of common linen, strapped and fastened with many ribbons; and, from underneath a rough chemise, stood out two full and hard breasts with deep-red nipples.

Katerina, the never-smiling, grinned. It was the kind of bust she was looking for. The wide skirt of flowered and cheap material fell to the floor and a pair of wide trousers, reaching to the ankles, came to view. A bush of thick black hair protruded through the open slit of the drawers, which was there for the sake of commodity.

Soon skirt and drawers were also removed and Katerina eyed her find with growing satisfaction. She went around and around the nude girl. The waistline was perfect; the legs full and female, but subtle; and the flesh of the ass seemed to be even softer than that of her mistress. To find out, she came close to the girl and felt her body. She was content. This was not the usual peasant type. This was not a tough and common brat. This girl had the form of an aristocrat.

Katerina remembered her measurements, took out her ribbons and began her comparisons. Well, the height was almost perfect – a little too tall, but she could tolerate that small difference. The length of the back, the breasts, the waistline, the thickness of the thighs were right, or what one might call right. Even the wrists and the ankles fitted. It turned out that the length of the legs, measured from the slit to the floor, was a trifle too long, but Katerina had already resolved that this girl was most suitable.

When the last measurement was taken and Katerina, kneeling on the floor, had touched the pussy, the girl had drawn slightly and irritatedly back. For the rest, she had behaved quietly and with an absence of that shamefulness or shyness characteristic of other girls. These girls did not know of the existence of anything like shame.

The bargaining started. Katerina wanted to hire only the dark girl and she did not want to pay more than fifty rubles; the blonde imp was not wanted. The cousin shrieked that then she didn't need to hire the dark girl either. While Katerina zealously defended the money of her master, the blonde girl leaned against the table and the nude dark one stood motionless in the middle of the room with hanging arms, as if she had nothing to do with the affair. The driver here and there interjected an appeasing word from the door, where he loitered as a witness waiting for a handsome commission. The cousin was thin and hard. Katerina was eager to get what she wanted and, after a battle, the old housekeeper's hand went into the bodice which covered her enormous bosom and brought to light an ugly leather purse, from which she paid the cousin ninety rubles in glittering gold. She had beaten the fee down from the demanded hundred, but she had to hire both girls.

No, she was not sending a carriage for them. She was going to take both with her. She was afraid she might lose her precious discovery. They would start immediately. The girls had nothing to pack. They had no belongings except some woollen kerchiefs and the like, which were quickly made into a bundle. After the dark girl was hurriedly dressed again, Katerina took a quick leave with her hirelings, though not without assuring the cousin anew that the fee requested had been outrageous. The cousin made the sign of the cross over the departing girls. They, in turn, automatically and without feeling kissed the hem of her dress and soon the three women sat in the carriage. The driver was paid a little distance from Sokolow's house and received what he demanded. It is quite sure that, with this money and the commission from his cousin, he was senselessly drunk for several days afterward.

Starting toward the palace, Katerina asked the dark girl what her name was. 'Grushenka,' answered the girl, readily. That was the first word she spoke after becoming one of the uncounted souls in the employ of Prince Alexey Sokolow. She did not know then the name of her new master.

Peter the Great had done away with the seclusion of women who had lived until then the Oriental life of the harem. He had forced them into society, where they were at first so awkward that he had had to get them drunk in order to loosen them up. He had lifted the aristocratic caste to an elevated position by forcing the working class into unheard-of servitude and submission. He had by the most cruel tortures, in which he participated personally, built up a social order in which might was god and the serf a slave. He had forced Western culture upon his nobles and one of his orders had been that they should build themselves great castles and houses.

Alexey Sokolow was only a score of years the junior of this great ruler. While eager to take all the advantages which were offered to his class, he had enough cunning to see that it was wiser to stay away from the inner court circle, where the greatest generals and high officials were uncertain as to when they would find themselves on the rack or the wheel and eventually beheaded. Sokolow had therefore established his city life in Moscow instead of St Petersburg, and in Moscow he had erected the magnificent palace which can be seen to this day.

Katerina dismissed the droshky a few blocks away, so as not to be seen by other servants riding in a hired carriage, and she led the two bewildered girls to the huge arch of the main entrance, which was guarded by two soldiers with muskets, high tin helmets and high boots. They paid no attention to the three women who quickly entered the archway and were admitted to the inner courtyard.

Flowers, lampions, grass, even bushes, covered the tremendous square of the inner court. Tables, chairs and benches stood about in great disorder. This courtyard was normally a barren place of cobblestones, but the princess had given an entertainment the night before for which the flowers and grass had been raised in hothouses in the country.

Katerina gave her wards no time to look or to think. She hurried them through the court and down a stone staircase to the basement, which consisted of endless halls and rooms and kitchens. Here Katerina left the blonde girl with a woman who seemed to be an overseer of this underground labyrinth. She then took Grushenka by the hand and marched on with her. This time she led her up a small and winding wooden staircase, which ended at the second floor. Thick Turkish carpets covered the light hallway and Grushenka soon saw a room which she was going to know very thoroughly afterwards. It was the dressing room of the princess, furnished with a big oak table in the middle and huge chestnut closets and presses along the walls, between which mirrors of all kinds had been installed.

On a curt order from Katerina, the girl took all her clothes off and, entirely nude, was led by the old housekeeper through other rooms, which were magnificently adorned with silks and brocades. Through the half-open door of her mistress's boudoir, Katerina led the substitute of madam. In her excitement, she didn't wait for permission to enter.

The princess was sitting before a mirror at her toilet table. Boris, the coiffeur, was busy curling her long, dark-brown hair. A young serf girl knelt on the floor and put rouge on her mistress's toenails. In the corner, near a window, sat 'Fräulein', an elderly spinster who had been a German governess in different houses of the great and who was now reading aloud in a dry and monotonous voice some French poetry. The princess listened with slight understanding or interest. The poet had worked into his fable all kinds of persons from Greek and Latin mythology, which meant nothing to the capricious listener. But when he described how the enormous shaft of Mars was pushed into the grotto of Venus, that called for noticeable attention.

In her mirror Princess Nelidowa had seen Katerina appear with Grushenka and waved angrily not to be disturbed. So Grushenka had an opportunity to study the group just described. The princess wore only a short batiste chemise which left her more or less uncovered. She did not mind that Boris, clad in the formal house uniform of the Sokolows, with a long pigtail at his back, could see her nudity, because he was only a serf. He had been sent to Dresden some years ago to learn the art of hairdressing with a very famous master in the Saxonian capital. Sokolow had intended to rent him out to one of the ladies' hairdressing parlours recently opened in Moscow, but the princess had taken the clever fellow into her private service. He was responsible for her many tufts and locks worn in the daytime and for her powdered wigs, decorated with precious stones, which went with the evening gowns.

When the reading of the poem ceased, Katerina could restrain herself no longer. 'I have her! I have her!' she cried and dragged Grushenka closer to the princess. 'I found a substitute who fits perfectly and she is ours now!'

'I know you could have found her sooner,' said Nelidowa maliciously. 'But you'll be forgiven since you dug her up at last. Now show me, does she really have the same measurements that I have or are you lying to me?' She rose hastily from her stool, so that poor Boris was in danger of burning her with his hot irons.

'She truly fits,' answered Katerina. 'Here, I'll show you.' And she took out the multicoloured ribbons to prove the fact. But Nelidowa was not interested in that. With sharp eyes she scrutinised Grushenka's body and was not dissatisfied.

'So that is how I look! A full pair of good breasts, aren't they? But mine are better!' – and taking out, without concern, her own breasts from her thin shirt and holding them close to Grushenka's, she started a minute comparison – 'Mine are oval and that is rare, but this slob's are round. Look at her nipples! How big and common!' – and she tickled with her own nipples those of the girl.

Now it is true that there was a slight difference, but hardly noticeable. Nelidowa then took hold of Grushenka's waist with both hands and did not handle her too tenderly.

'I always said,' the mistress continued, 'that I have an excellent waistline, and here one can see it. Among all the court ladies, not one can compare with me.'

That it was not her own waistline she admired, but that of her new girl, did not come to her mind. She proceeded to the thighs, which she pinched, and was surprised by Grushenka's very soft flesh. 'My legs,' she commented, displaying now her own thighs and squeezing them a bit, 'are sturdier than those of this little bitch, but we'll take the softness out of her.' With mock laughter, she commanded Grushenka to turn around.

Nelidowa, like Grushenka, had a remarkably well-modelled back:

round female shoulders, soft and full lines down to the bottom, small and well-rounded hips. Only Grushenka's buttocks were too small, almost boyish, and went too evenly and straight to the thighs. Her legs and feet were normal and straight and could have been used by artists as models.

'Now!' laughed the princess. 'This is the first time that I see my own back and truly I like it. Isn't it fine that this tramp should have just my back?'

The witnesses of this scene, especially Katerina, were astonished by the similarity between these two women as they stood close together. It was astounding to see that not only their figures but their features and faces were so much alike that one could have sworn they were twin sisters. Nature sometimes plays tricks of that kind. Grushenka was younger; she had a whiter skin; she blushed in her excitement and looked fresher. Also, her flesh was softer and a bit more feminine-looking than that of Nelidowa, and she had a timid bearing and was not so self-contained as the princess. Otherwise, they were strangely alike, though no one would have dared to tell this to the princess.

'I am pleased with you and I'll present you with my new prayer book with the pictures of the saints in it, which you admired the other day. It's yours. Go and get it.' Katerina, with a deep curtsy, kissed her mistress's hand, overjoyed that she had at last satisfied her. She was taking the girl out of the room when she was stopped by a parting injunction from her mistress, who watched the nude form depart.

'By the way, Katerina, have all the hair under her arms and on her dirty cunt removed so that she doesn't infect my garments. And have her spotlessly washed and powdered. You know how filthy these pigs are.' Katerina assured her she would have the girl properly bathed, groomed and dressed.

A few days later, Grushenka had to show her mistress a new costume, a light-blue, fluffy affair with many ribbons and laces. The princess had liked it and incidentally had ordered the girl to show her cunt. Grushenka lifted the costume carefully in front, and another girl spread the slit of her trousers open, while the princess took a good look. Nelidowa was thinking that if that pussy before her eyes should be used often, the rosy and thin lips would certainly become thick and vulgar. Hence, the order to Katerina that Grushenka was to be fucked daily and that Katerina should supply various men in order that the business be attended to properly.

Grushenka was delighted to hear it, but Katerina disliked this new order, for which she could not imagine the reason. She moved

Grushenka's bed to a separate room in the basement and, after dinner, gave the girl her instructions. First she gave her a salve and ordered her to smear it every day after dinner into her vagina. This salve was to kill the sperm. The irrigations, to be taken afterward, would make doubly sure that she should not get an enlarged belly.

Presently she sent a young stableman to the girl's room, a red-haired, freckled, undersized man, who grinned with delight. When the call had come to the stable, the men threw dice for the trick and the redhead was much envied when he won.

Grushenka was sitting on her bed when he entered the room. She held one hand over her breasts; the other clutched her thin dress in front. She was very beautiful and the stableman promised to be careful and explained to her, being a nice chap, that if she followed his suggestions, they could both enjoy it profoundly.

Grushenka promised to do all he said and he proceeded with great care. He tickled her pussy with the point of his shaft for a while and then inserted it by degrees, moving always a bit back and shuffling it in again, each time more, until his hair rubbed closely against her well-shaven mount of Venus. He then enquired whether it had hurt and Grushenka answered in a soft, wondering voice, 'Just a bit. Do be careful.'

But it had not hurt her at all. It was just a funny feeling, not exactly exciting, but pleasing. He told her to move her ass slowly up and down, which she did, while he lay stiff and strong, until he started to heave and push, finally forgetting himself and fucking quite to his heart's content. Grushenka did not answer his strokes, but she held her arms close to his back and, when he finally came, she pressed her cunt firmly against his belly and felt satisfaction when his hot scum spread into her insides.

He had not had enough. He stayed in her bed, joking with her. He played around with her breasts and her cunt, laughed to see that she was shaved and pinched her bottom good-heartedly. She was amazed at how quickly he got stiff again and she did not fight him off when he put his prick in anew. This time her nervousness was gone. Still she did not get a thrill out of it, although it felt rather pleasant – even more pleasant than the first time.

This time he had to work harder to get the load out of his balls. She assisted him very little, although she caressed his back with her hand shyly and tried to make her cunt as tight as possible, so that the slippery machine down there could get as much friction as possible. After he had come, she started to move and to heave. She wanted something more now herself, but he slipped his tired love-shaft out of her. She was tired and slept so soundly that they had a hard time getting her up next morning.

Every night after dinner, a man came to fuck her. Sometimes they were elderly and did not undress but just laid her over the bed and fucked her and disappeared. Sometimes they were hardly older than Grushenka and so shy that she had a great time teasing them and working them up and finally seducing them so many times that they walked from the room with weak knees.

Grushenka learned to love fucking more than she ever had before coming to the palace. She learned to get the supreme thrill with every man; half a dozen times if she liked her partner. She learned how to make love and soon became a passionate lover. The male servants in the house, most of whom tried her out, praised her with glittering eyes. What a girl! What a figure! What a piece of ass! A volcano!

These were fine weeks, weeks of thrills, weeks during which her body filled out and her mind became clear, weeks without dreams, full of reality. She looked at other girls with searching curiosity. She learned from them about their love affairs. She studied her mistress with appraising eyes. Couldn't she manage to get a nice husband and a little house with some acres and have children, too? Why not? She learned who was influencing the master and the mistress; she made plans; she laid eyes on one of the best body servants of the prince and, though she never spoke with him or had intercourse with him, she believed she had fallen in love with him. All that ended of a sudden, however, and it was again her mistress who affected the change, her mistress who was by right and law Grushenka's destiny.

Nelidowa used to start many things, giving many orders, and then forgetting about them again. Her mind wandered. Everything was done in a haphazard way. But Nelidowa remembered one night, when she came from the bedroom of her husband, after working over his prick for some time, that Grushenka had been her means of finding out how a cunt would change by frequent fucking – so she sent for her.

Grushenka had had a quick and meaningless poke from an elderly man that night about an hour before and was still awake when the handmaiden of Nelidowa came for her. She put a bed sheet around her shoulders and walked nude and barefoot to Her Highness's bedchamber. (It must be remembered that all people, high or low, male or female, slept without nightshirts at that time, and it is said that Marie Antoinette, some fifty years later, was the first one to create the mode.) Nelidowa had just washed her pussy and was sitting naked before her toilet table while one of her maids braided her long dark-brown hair into pigtails.

Nelidowa was in a good mood and told Grushenka to wait until her hair was done. In a few minutes, she took the nude girl on her lap. She enquired whether Grushenka had been poked daily, whether the pricks had been big and long, whether she had learned to fuck properly and whether she liked it. Grushenka automatically answered yes to every question. Then Nelidowa gently parted the girl's legs and examined her pussy.

There was no change to be seen. The little love-nest was tender and innocent, as though it had never held big male machines. The lips were perhaps more red, and fuller, but still firmly closed and thin. The princess opened them and fingered the girl, who quivered under this caress. The princess parted her own legs a little and wondered at her own cunt, which was wide open with thick flappy lips. Apparently it was not fucking but the hand of nature which had made the difference between their cunts.

* * *

Grushenka stretched herself in Martha's four-posted bed. Martha had kissed her goodbye and left for work. Grushenka slept and day-dreamed. She got up lazily and put on her peasant dress, leaving her fine travelling dress in Martha's closet. She put all her money, except one ruble, on the mantelpiece, said a word of goodbye to her absent girlfriend and left the house with slow steps.

She did not want to think of the future. She walked leisurely to the border of the city, went through the gate where some Cossacks loitered and found her way to the Moscow River. She sat on the bank of the river, let her eyes go over the wide plain and observed, without much attention, the peasants harvesting the fields. The waters of the wide river flowed down in easy rhythm. Far away some boys and girls were swimming.

Grushenka dreamt, as only a Russian peasant can dream, a thought-less and wordless dream, uniting herself with the soil, becoming a part of it, losing the sense of place or time. When the sun dropped lower on the horizon, she got up and slowly returned to the city. She stopped in a public house where she ate a bowl of soup and some bread and cheese. The few customers and the innkeeper hardly noticed this peasant girl with her lovely face hidden beneath a kerchief. Back again on the street, she pulled herself up with an energetic nod of her head and walked with quick steps to Ladislaus Brenna's establishment. She had never been inside that place, but she knew all about it.

Ladislaus Brenna ran a famous bathing establishment for middle-class people and Grushenka had made up her mind to become a bath attendant. She would have liked to get such a job with one of the new and elegant bathhouses patronised by the fashionable world, but she did not dare to do so, as she might be found out. No one would look for her in Brenna's.

After she opened the door, she stood immediately in the big bath hall for men. The hall took up the whole ground floor of the building.

On a white wooden floor stood forty to fifty wooden bathtubs in irregular arrangement. In one of these tubs the bather sat on a little bench, the water coming up to his neck. A few customers were bathing; others were reading, writing on little boards put over the tubs, playing board games with each other or just chatting.

Brenna sat on the opposite side of the room behind an elevated bar. Grushenka lost no time, but went right over to him while the eyes of all the bathers and attendants followed her. She stated without shyness that she wanted to become one of his bath girls. Brenna looked sharply at her and ordered her to wait. He was a whale of a fellow, about forty-five years old. His hairy chest, open to view, and his wild black beard exaggerated his tousled appearance. Grushenka sat down on a wooden bench and looked around with curiosity. Brenna's place was supposed to be full of fun for its visitors, men and women alike, but most housewives disapproved violently when they heard that their husbands or grown-up sons frequented it.

Grushenka's attention was first directed toward the bath attendants, about ten girls, some sitting on a bench near the big open fireplace, others moving about the big room pursuing their duties. All the girls were nude except for wooden slippers and here and there a short apron or towel around the hips. Any kind of clothes would have been annoying in this air, heavy with steam and dampness. They were all husky, rather good-looking girls and seemed in good spirits and satisfied. They carried buckets of hot water to the occupied bathtubs, pouring it in to keep the temperature even. They brought beer or tea or other refreshments to the men, laughed and joked with them and did not seem to mind when the men felt their breasts or their pussies. When one of the customers wanted to get out of his tub, they opened up the linen top, placed a footstool and helped the man out. Then they followed him into one of the many cabinets which lined the walls. Grushenka could well imagine what happened inside them.

The last customer having left, the girls began to clean up while Brenna admonished them to take their time and do a thorough job. He had a gruff voice, but one could feel that he was a good sort. At last he turned to Grushenka and ordered her to follow him. They went upstairs, passing the women's bath hall on the second floor and passing the third floor where Brenna lived with his family. When they reached the attic, Brenna pushed open a door leading into an unoccupied room furnished with a large wooden bed, a washstand and two chairs.

'Well,' he said, 'I will look you over to see whether you are strong enough to carry the water and to give a massage. I could use a bitch like you, but you seem to be too weak. Show me what you've got.'

With that, he went to the little window and looked out into the twilight. His huge frame in front of the window shut out almost all the light from the room. Grushenka quickly got rid of her clothes and stood nude in the middle of the room, waiting for him to pass his judgement. She was now a bit nervous. What would happen to her if he did not employ her?

Brenna gazed for quite a while out into the sunset. Finally he turned around to her, moved away from the window and put her in a position where the slowly fading light fell directly on her. He was amazed at her fine figure; her full breasts especially attracted him. Her straight legs and firm thighs did not displease him. He felt the muscles of her arms, pinched her bottom and the flesh above the knees the way one feels the leg of a horse, while she contracted her muscles as well as she could in order to appear strong. He moved her around again, uncertain whether a girl with such a small waistline would be suited to his type of work, and fixed his eyes on her mound of Venus. Grushenka was a well-built girl, above medium height, but before this giant of a man she felt rather small just when she wished to be big.

He asked her to lie on the bed and spread her legs. She quickly complied, knowing what the final test would be. He opened up his linen trousers and took out a mighty and hard, blown-up prick. She was ready when he bent forward, rested his weight on his hands next to her shoulders and moved his prick toward her entrance. She lowered her hands to insert his shaft and was surprised at its huge dimensions; she could hardly span it with her hand. She wanted to insert it carefully, but before she had a chance, he pushed it in with a mighty stroke. Grushenka answered with a heavy groan. It hadn't hurt her, but it filled her to the utmost and stretched her cunt to the limit.

It had been a few days since she had had intercourse, but some of the scenes she had witnessed of late had served to stimulate her desire.

Therefore this unexpected pleasure brought her to a fever heat. She raised her legs high above his massive back. She thrust herself against his prick with all her power, encircling his love-instrument with the full suction of her cunt. She crushed her fingers into his muscular arms and began to fuck him with everything in her.

She closed her eyes. All kinds of lascivious pictures went through her mind; she remembered the first time so long ago; she thought of the various men who had given her satisfaction; finally the angelic features of her Mihail stood out clearly, telling her how much he adored her.

All this time she was working with strong pushes against those of her partner while she circled her bottom around as belly dancers do. Gradually her whole body became more and more contorted until only her shoulders touched the bed as she strove to find the best position in which to fuck. Her body was covered with sweat, her hair became loose and partially covered her face, her mouth twisted, her heels pressed upon his back and his buttocks. At last, with an outcry, she felt her great climax come. Then she lay motionless, heavily breathing, all her muscles loose. Her bottom dropped upon the mattress and Brenna's prick fell out.

Brenna lay on his hands, hardly moving; he was satisfied with the vitality this girl displayed. So satisfied, in fact, that he was not ready to let her go right now, especially since his prick was again as swollen and red as it had been.

'Eh, little hussy,' he interrupted her after-love dreams, 'don't stop now. My little fellow down there is still stiff and angry.'

Grushenka opened her eyes to find herself staring into this gruff face surrounded with flowing black hair. An utterly strange face it was to her, with black eyes, a short broad nose and full lascivious lips. Still, somehow, there was a sense of humour about it which took the sting out of its roughness. She gazed into this face and it came to her mind how much she had enjoyed satisfying this man. By her uncontrolled passion she had given him a wonderful time; now she would give him a still better time by her thorough knowledge of the art of fucking.

Dutifully she put her legs up on his back, this time moving them even higher, so that she almost touched his shoulders with her heels – whereby Master Prick slipped back of his own accord into his former kingdom.

She grasped his head with her hands and moved it down. His feet slid slowly backwards and he soon lay with his whole weight on her. She now lay on her back at full length and so had better means of wiggling her bottom under him. Then she arched herself under him and, moving her right hand down, managed to get hold of his balls. She proceeded to caress and finger his testicles with soft strokes, at the same time tickling the inside of his ear with the little finger of her left hand.

He put his right hand under her small bottom – so large was this hand, that he was able to hold both cheeks with one clasp – and began in slow strokes to do his work. He pushed his sceptre deep into her cunt so that it touched her womb, moved slowly back to the outer entrance and repeated this play in regular rhythm. She moved her behind in circles with her eyes wide open. She was aware of every move and this enabled her to give him her fullest cooperation. When he got really hot, however, he forgot himself entirely. He got back on his feet, standing close to the bed, and raised her behind up so that her head and shoulders hardly touched the linen. Holding her by her hips, he connected with her only by the contact between prick and pussy and he fucked her with all his might. She felt him come! She felt a hot flood of sperm shooting into her and, strange to say, she came again.

As unexpectedly as he had pleasured her, he now let her go and her behind fell to the edge of the bed. In a matter-of-fact way he put his still stiff prick back into his trousers. He took another look at her and liked her. Her feet touched the floor, her legs were still half open. One of her hands lay above her black-haired pussy, the coral lips of which protruded; the other hand rested on her full breast. Her mouth was a bit open, her deep black eyelashes shadowed her steel-blue eyes, her hair hung around her face. The girl was so beautiful that he felt like giving her another fuck. He bent down and felt the soft flesh of her thighs. His guests would like this trollop.

'Wash up, and get ready for supper,' he said with resolution. 'I'll try you out. You might do.'

He opened the door and called for Gargarina. The attic was the living quarters for all the girls employed in the house and they had come up in the meantime to dress. Presently Gargarina came in and was ordered by Brenna to break in the new girl to her job. He left without further explanation.

Gargarina was an older girl, about twenty-five years of age, tall, blonde and husky. She had a shirt on and was just about to button her long lacy drawers. She looked at Grushenka with a certain curiosity. Grushenka sat on the edge of the bed, weak but not exhausted, and scratched herself thoughtfully along the soft flesh of her belly and thighs.

Gargarina said: 'Well, he looked you over, didn't he? He certainly has the best prick in the whole neighbourhood and we ought to know. I can imagine how you feel. It's almost four years since I came here and he just killed me. After that, he told me that he could not use me. That's the way with most girls who apply for work here; he tries them all. We thought he would send you away, too. You know, I just stayed on and came to work the next morning. He yelled at me to get out, but I know how it is with a stray dog. He just couldn't get rid of me and that was four years ago.'

'I don't know what I would have done, as I have no other place to go, either.'

'Never mind that now. It's that way with most of us girls here, except those of us who were brought by their parents. One of the girls was brought by her husband. He was drafted for the army, and where can the poor creature go until his seven years are over? She doesn't know whether he'll ever come back. He was last heard of in Siberia. He can't write, you see, and she can't read.'

'Oh!' answered Grushenka with a flicker of pride. 'I can read and write.'

'That's fine!' retorted Gargarina kindly. 'Then you'll be able to read us some stories out of books and write our love letters for us. You will be quite a busy person with that. But now you'd better clean out your pussy' – and she looked at the sperm which ran out of the love-nest and wet Grushenka's legs – 'because you couldn't serve down in the bath hall with a swollen belly.'

She brought her a bowl of water and a towel. Grushenka sat down on the floor with the bowl, wrapped the end of the towel around a finger, inserted it in her orifice and rubbed herself. Gargarina, who was watching her, remarked, 'Tomorrow, I'll show you a better way to get your pussy clean. But now dress quickly. Dinner will be ready in a minute.'

When Grushenka came down to the dining room, she regretted that she had left her fine travelling dress at Martha's. All the other girls were dressed up fit to kill and her peasant dress looked rather out of place. There were twice as many girls as she had seen downstairs, the additional ones being those who served in the bath for women. They all sat around a long table. At one end Mr Brenna presided; at the other end sat his wife. She was a very small thin woman of over forty with a sharp pointed nose, and looked like a greedy and hardened spinster. But she certainly did not take it out on the girls in regard to food. Two strapping maids served a rich meal, no less good and healthy than Katerina, Princess Nelidowa's housekeeper, provided for her wards. The girls hurried through their meal, anxious to leave. Only two or three stayed home that night; the rest had rendezvous. For police identification, each girl carried a permit issued by Brenna.

Grushenka chatted with the girls remaining in the attic. She learned that room and board was all Brenna paid for their services, but that they made many, sometimes good, tips. They all were satisfied and, while they were rough and used strong words, they seemed to get along in good-hearted comradeship. Grushenka went to bed early, quite tired.

The next morning she was up many hours before being called to breakfast. Brenna's place opened after noon, the first guests arriving only after two or three, and the whole job was done by seven in the evening. The arrival of any customer was signalled by the young fellow in the doorway, who incidentally had charge of the large stove in the basement that supplied the hot water, the heat in wintertime and the steam for the steam room. He rapped with a stick against the door and when he rapped a few times that meant a man of money and a good tipper. All the men were more or less known to all.

Grushenka, taken in tow by Gargarina, lined up with the other girls near the entrance and solicited the entering man. It meant tips and the more customers a girl could get, so much the better for her. Sometimes the girls fought over the customers and that was the only thing Brenna would not stand for. He would mutter curses and the girls were afraid.

The first man who came in looked like a poet. He wore a long flowing necktie and was young and blond. Gargarina told Grushenka not to try to attract his attention because he had a steady girl, a plump dark-haired creature with big soft breasts. This girl took him by the hand and led him into one of the cabinets where they remained for a long while. Gargarina explained to Grushenka that he was a writer on a gazette and came every afternoon to save the soul of the dark girl. However, his sermon always ended sexually.

Next came a wealthy coachman who kept many carriages and gave good tips. All the girls besieged him, but Gargarina and Grushenka had no luck. He was followed by a baker who was Gargarina's steady customer, and the two girls went with him into a cabinet. Gargarina said that she had to break in the 'new girl'.

The baker was a sturdy short man, with snow-white hair, bristly and unkempt. As soon as the door was closed, Gargarina started to make love to him, but he would have nothing of it. The girls undressed him leisurely. He wore no stockings but a kind of undergarment of cheap cotton, which he slipped off himself. Meanwhile he told them that he was damn tired. After getting through with his baking job, beginning at nine at night and finishing at three in the morning, his old lady had wakened and forced him to give her three rides.

His prick vouched for his statement; it hung sadly downward. In spite of his protest Gargarina insisted on giving him a massage and he lay down reluctantly on the massage table. Gargarina took a handful of liquid soap and began to knead his flesh. She told Grushenka to do the same and, while she had one side of his behind and legs in operation, Grushenka started timidly with the other half. Seeing how hard her teacher worked, she put her whole weight into her hands and soon found herself sweating. When his back was done and he was turned over, she avoided touching his testicles. This amused Gargarina, who, taking the limp prick in her hand, made a thousand jokes about a penis.

The baker paid no attention to this chatter. He got up from the table before they were really through with him and walked over to a tub, which they filled with hot water. The linen was pulled over him, he leaned back and soon was soundly snoring. During the following hours, without waking him up, they kept pouring hot water into the tub, first carefully taking a bucketful of water out of it.

A few more men entered, but other girls got hold of them. Then came a tall thin man whom none of the girls wanted. Grushenka held herself back instinctively. It was just her luck that he selected her. Gargarina stepped right up explaining that the new girl was under her supervision. As all three entered a cabinet together, Gargarina whispered that this one was a pest.

He behaved in a very orderly way while they undressed him, telling Grushenka that he was the scribe with the new judge and that he came from St Petersburg where it was the newest fad with the ladies to paint their nipples red. After he was naked he embraced Grushenka, pulled her tightly to his lean body and, running his long fingers up and down her spine, told her how beautiful she was and how soft her flesh felt. Meanwhile he pressed one of his thighs between hers and rubbed his prick against the soft flesh of her leg. Soon enough his love-instrument became stiff and Grushenka felt that it was very thin and very long. He then put one finger in Grushenka's cunt and began to frig her.

Gargarina had meanwhile gone behind him and embraced him from behind, rubbing her breasts on his back and her pussy on his behind. She leaned her head over one of his shoulders just as Grushenka did, and both girls were almost mouth to mouth. Gargarina made faces indicating haste, but at first Grushenka did not mind his playing with her. He had apt fingers and always managed to tickle just the right spot. As she became more excited, she showed it on her face and her pussy got wet. Her ass came slowly into swing. The scribe had his other hand on her behind, but another idea struck him. He told her to take firm hold of him and, leaving one hand in her pussy, extended his other hand back until he found Gargarina's love-nest and began to frig her also. Gargarina, who knew him already, fucked that finger right away as if she was terribly excited. They squirmed violently as he frigged faster and faster, then both came together. At last he grew tired of this playing around and left them to take a bath. But he tipped them both very generously, and Grushenka thought she would like working at Brenna's.

5

Crimson Hairs

1934

Crimson Hairs by the pseudononymous 'Whidden Graham' is an American original. First published in 1934, and quickly reprinted in 1938, it is an erotic mystery tale that is explicitly sexual.

The time is during Prohibition, and homicide detective Morris Sarnelli, known as 'Handsome' to the girls, takes special personal interest in a mysterious corpse found in the basement of a brownstone in New York's fashionable West 60s. Certain unsolved aspects of the case, sexual aspects to Sarnelli's mind, cause him to pursue the investigation on his own. The detective is slowly drawn into New York's sexual underground as he makes his case. Conducting floor-by-floor interviews with the occupants of the murder scene, he discovers their sexual peccadilloes, and enters into one strange sexual experience after the other. No clue, nor aspect of human sexuality is left untouched.

Aficionados of the 1930s' detective thrillers will recognise the language and style of the story. The detective reminds one of Mike Hammer in a more libertine and uninhibited mood than usual. The action is fast paced, the slang true to the times, and the 'mystery' sometimes is placed on hold as the characters' love lives get the better of them. By the time the murderer is found out, no one really cares; the sex has taken precedence.

✎ from *Crimson Hairs*

Sarnelli woke up the next morning refreshed and unperturbed. The adventure with Rita had disgusted more than stirred him. He had seen too many nude women and they offered themselves to him too easily. To hell with them all. What he was angry about was that he had made no progress whatever in his case. He had to call up the Inspector and tell him about it. It was annoying. The Carr fellow was a clue. He wished he knew more about him. The man was highly intelligent and cagey. Did he really go around with women now or was that just to distract the detective's attention? There were many who were bisexual. Better have a talk with those girls downstairs. If Carr could release his dark and Oriental passion with females, or into females, then he was not under much suspicion, for he could more easily free himself from the fairies. Rita certainly had nothing to do with the case, and Edna and Bertha had to be eliminated also. They were not persons who would commit a violent deed themselves, nor did they consort with persons of uncontrolled temperaments. The same might be said for the janitress and her friend Francisca.

After breakfast Sarnelli went down to the basement. He searched the premises again and again. All of a sudden, he was startled. Somebody must have been in there. The water was dripping from the faucet. Oh, and there – that pile of junk had been touched. Nay, it had been washed, it seemed. In fact, several of the pieces were still a bit wet. What did that mean? The janitress, confronted with those facts, disputed hotly that anybody could have been in the cellar. It was locked now and the keys were in the hands of the detective and herself alone. Her key was hanging on the wall, right over there by the pot, in case any of the police should drop in and want to see the basement again. Sarnelli agreed that he might be seeing things. But he was sure now that somebody connected with the case was living right here in the house and had a reason for tinkering around downstairs. Why? Washing off fingerprints? Prints on things in the junk pile? He went downstairs again and studied the pile. He could not see the connections as yet. Well, patience was the first duty of a sleuth. It was with a mental reservation that he phoned to Inspector McGarven that he was probably right about it being a suicide case. No clues, no. But he would like to stay on a bit longer. That was granted, especially because

McGarven said to himself that the boy had something up his sleeve.

Time had passed with all this but it was still too early to call on Paula Eltz. She was a kept girl and slept late. After a walk, though, it was time to see her.

She answered his ring with repeated enquiries of 'Who is there?' before she opened the door quite reluctantly. Of course, she would have a talk with him and help him in any way she could, but she did not know anything and her attitude showed that she wanted to be left alone. Intending not to let her get away with it, he sat down for a stay. Paula refused all personal questions with the reply that she would have to see her lawyer as to whether she must answer at all.

Paula was about twenty-three years old, with light brown hair that was probably dyed. She was a good-looking bitch of medium height. Her mouth showed that she had been through plenty and was hard-boiled. But her grey-blue eyes had stamina and temperament. Sarnelli decided to become personal and complimented her on her tasteful pyjamas, her lovely complexion, and made a play for her with a charming and boyish grin, which usually took the women in quickly enough. But she remained taciturn and annoyed.

'Well, young lady, I'm sorry you dislike me so much personally, and I hope I haven't done anything to offend you. I wish you'd help me along a bit ...'

'I dislike dicks, that's all.'

'What have they done to you?'

'Plenty ... I mean, nothing – nothing at all. I just dislike the whole bunch of them. Any other questions? Or can we end our conversation now?'

Sarnelli made a quick shift in attack: 'You know I'm from headquarters and, of course, we looked up everybody before we started this investigation. We looked you up also, of course.'

'So what?'

'Nothing ... We know. That's all. The neighbourhood here does not know and you're just a charming young lady who has a still more charming friend with a pocketbook. You see, that's something that does not concern us, but ...'

Paula became rather hysterical at once. She became pale and squirmed around.

'I have no money and if I had any, I would not give it to you. I wouldn't. Understand? I wouldn't.'

Sarnelli pricked his ears. So this dame had a past? Really better look up her record, if she is not living under an assumed name. He smiled:

'Lady, that must surprise you. I do not want any money. I do not need it, thank you, and I would not take it from anyone, most certainly not from a woman.'

'That's what you dicks are after. What else are you living on, you . . . ' She started to cry but caught herself and looked bravely up at him. Sarnelli saw the change in her attitude.

'If I meet a nice young lady like you, I do not take her money. I always like to give her some. See . . . ' And he displayed a small bankroll from his pocket.

'Marked money, eh?'

This time he laughed heartily. Then he explained to her that he had nothing whatever to do with the boys from the vice squad, that he considered the prosecution of prostitution a terrible legal mistake. Prostitution was one of the oldest and most lucrative businesses in the world and, if run in an orderly way, a blessing to men. But when conducted under hypocritical laws, secretly, it was a curse to everyone. She agreed to all this and looked at him. His frank speech and manly looks appealed to her and she offered him a cigarette. This little token was the beginning of the friendship. In the most casual way, he took her hand and drew her on to his lap. Soon enough he knew all there was to know about her.

Rent, food, clothes and about thirty to forty dollars per week was what her friend paid. A decent businessman, easy to handle, never drunk. Only she never knew when she might be wanted. He called her up when he desired to see her and made a date that she had to keep strictly on time. Of course, he collected what he was paying for. She had been steady with him for two years and had been true to him. Yes, she knew different madames who would have liked to have her name on their phone lists, but why jeopardise a comfortable arrangement. She had something on her mind: Supposing a girl had been once in a jam, quite innocently, when she was still dumb, and supposing there was a record of her in the police files, was there no way of getting that record destroyed? He gave her advice and promised to help her. She was really a nice kid, he would say, a decent kid. She warmed up to him. She felt he meant what he said and that he was a swell guy. Before they knew it, they hugged and kissed each other, at first more in the way of play or a joke, but after that, real desire came into the picture.

She tickled his ears with kisses, and he started feeling her full breasts, until his hand reached for her pussy. She whispered: 'What's the use of struggling against it? Come on, let's have it. I'm going to give you the "grand treatment" and you are going to be a good boy and just keep still and do everything I say. I haven't done that to anyone for a long, long time. My boyfriend is so decent, you know, and he'd be shocked if he ever learned that his little flower – that's what he always calls me – even knows about such things.'

She slipped off his lap, pulled the shades down, ran to the front door and locked it, and dragged him into her bedroom. A cosy bedroom with black silken bed sheets that would appeal to every sensuous woman. Sarnelli hesitated for a moment. It certainly had not been his purpose to have a party now, but that was just his nature. When he felt like it, he forgot whether it was reasonable or not, and – why not?

She made him take all his clothes off and lie down on the bed, his hands folded behind his head. She did not allow him to touch her; she did not want to be disturbed, as she put it. She quickly removed her pyjamas and for a moment looked him over with greedy eyes. His naked form enticed her. Lean and tall, the figure of a sportsman, muscular and strong. She was glad she had captured him for her own pleasure; she liked men.

He, also, was quite satisfied. In the dim light her flesh showed white and soft; her nipples were very large and deep brown; the hair around her pussy was thin and of a blondish colour, while the lips of her cunt were open and looked hungry. Her bottom was too small for his taste, but her whole figure seemed soft and mobile. It would be a pleasure to be encircled by her.

She kissed his forehead and his face, took his lips in her mouth and kissed and bit them softly. Her hands stroked his body. It was an exciting massage she gave him – first his chest, while sucking his nipples, and then stroking his belly and continuing down over his muscular limbs. She massaged him with both her soft hands, with expert knowledge of the nerves, and already he had difficulty in keeping his buttocks from moving around. She kissed his belly and started to lick it with long strokes of her firm and apt tongue. Meanwhile, her hands played with the curls around his tool and tickled his balls. But she did not touch his love-shaft which stood full-blown and straight in the air, longing for a resting place. She ignored it entirely and teased him with prolonged appetite.

Then she made him turn over and the same procedure took place along his spine and over his firm ass-cheeks and thighs. Finally she settled down and sucked and licked and kissed him, so that he shivered through his whole body. It was almost torture but he stood it. Finally, she crawled into bed, sat straddle-legged over him and pressed her pussy against his neck. She bent forward and glued her mouth to his tool. She surprised him by giving it a long and passionate sucking. It was a long time since any woman had kissed him there. But this kid certainly was an artist. What a wonderful sensation a well-trained tongue could be! He was thoroughly thrilled and flushed all over.

Now she turned him around, moving his body in such a way that his feet were touching the carpet as he lay across the bed. Already she was kneeling before him. She slung his legs over her shoulders and, taking his prick in one hand, continued her tongue-play over his hairy balls. She inhaled the odour of his body, pressed her own thighs together and moved her bottom around. She was terribly excited herself and put everything she had into the act. At last she moved up a bit and embraced his stiff shaft again with her lips. Her lips closed more firmly than before around his magnificent tool and she sucked it into her mouth until it touched her throat. God, how she loved that! Up and down, up and down went her sucking mouth – and he worked softly against her, moving his bottom slightly. Changing the steady movements into circling and screwing movements, she groaned and purred and breathed convulsively.

That went on for a long time, until he could stand it no longer. He bent forward and, almost doubled-up, tried to grab her and get her into the bed. He wanted to fuck her now but she would not let him. She held his prick tightly with one hand, his balls with the other, while her mouth was glued to that precious instrument. His whole body shook.

'I can't stand it any longer!' he cried.

She released him for a moment. 'Then give it to me!' she said. 'I want to drink you! Give it to me!' And she was at it again.

He let himself fall back again and began fucking her mouth with strong moves. When he came and shot a mighty gusher, she released him at once. He wanted her to keep up the pressure on his spouting organ, but she had slipped out of the room and closed the door behind her. He shot a few drops into the air, but he was not wholly satisfied.

Presently she came back, cleaned him with a wet towel and slipped into bed with him, covering them both with the black silken sheet. She smiled and mocked him.

'You vixen! But you are an artist.' He stretched himself and drew her very close. 'How did you learn it – or is it a natural talent with you?'

'I might as well tell you the whole story, especially as I want you to help me get those records out of the files. Probably it is an old story for you, but here it is.' She nestled close and took his prick, now soft and lifeless, caressingly in her hand.

'I was not even nineteen when I came to the big city. Of course, I was not a virgin. I had some boyfriends in my hick town and here in the city, also, when I worked at odd jobs – as a salesgirl, model and so on. But I never took any money from my boyfriends. Presents, on the other hand, are always welcome, you know. As it happened, one day I found myself without a job and with very small funds. I had to look for a cheap room. The living quarters this beast – never mind her name – offered me were lovely and the price was only a couple of bucks. She explained that she was not really renting the room to me but liked to have the company of young girls, a line for which I fell. She was not a madame, but a procurer. I was much too dumb to find that out quick enough. Anyway, she sent me on some jobs to make "easy money" and here and there I went. Why deny it? Mostly I didn't follow her orders. I mean, from her standpoint, I was utterly unreliable. I can see that now. She and nobody else had me picked up by some dicks, with no evidence against me whatsoever, and they railroaded me by having me plead guilty. The six months in the reformatory were not as bad as everyone supposes, but when I was released my troubles began. No money, no friends no job . . . but one of the girls in the big house had given me the address of a madame, the best one in the business, they said, and to her I went, determined that she should take me in.

'I can still picture myself standing in her elegant drawing room, begging her to give me a chance. She did not want to have anything to do with a girl who had a record. She demanded highest ability, clever talk and frank immorality from her girls. She made me strip and felt me over and toyed around with me so that I really blushed. No woman had ever done such things to me. I had at that time very fine breasts – they are not so bad now, but then I must have been a morsel – and my little pussy was and is quite small. Other girls are much larger down there. Apparently she liked me. She began to praise her clientele, raved about the money I would make, drew fantastic pictures of magnificent clothes, and so on. But she stated that her customers were rich men, perverted and spoiled, and that a girl had to take it on the chin while working for her. I was still very dumb. She knew it and told me so, but she said I had talent and that she would put me through the mill.

'She showed me to one of her marvellously furnished rooms and let me wait there. She kept two or three steady girls in the house; the others were on call. A couple of hours later she came back with Carlos, her "tough guy", a kind of pimp, a swarthy, uncouth and lousy Italian fellow with one feature that was extraordinary: He could raise a hard-on and keep it for many hours. The girls said he was taking some herbs or a medicine that got him hot but hindered him from coming.

Anyway, the madame, who ordered him around as if he were a big animal, told him to put me through the mill. She sat down in an easy chair and smoked a cigarette and instructed me what to do. When I saw this huge, brown-skinned fellow sprawled on the bed, I was bewildered and did not know how to handle it.

'Anyway, when Carlos started to fuck me – gee! It was the toughest party I'd ever had. He was a husky, strong fellow and he pushed and pushed and forced me to answer his thrusts. Of course, I came and came and was finally all exhausted. So he took his big tool out of me and I had to kneel over him and suck it. Madame demanded that I make him come and, unaware that he couldn't, I worked like a fool. When my lips and my tongue were sore, I had to sit straddle-legged over him and ride him and then lick him again until I caved in. He sure put me through the mill. Madame finally ended the session and told me that I would do, but that I should understand that I was entirely under her supervision – and that was our agreement. I was much too exhausted to say anything but yes and I did not regret it in the long run.'

'There is lots of faking in those houses, isn't there?' Sarnelli asked rhetorically.

Somehow that was against Paula's pride. 'Not where I was. Oh no, sir. That was just the difference between my madame and the other bastards. She was in a way very straight. She never put anything over on anybody. She did not allow the girls to get extra money out of the men. She paid us our share. She paid the bulls what was coming to them. And we had to come across and do the right thing by the men. That's why she stayed so long unmolested in business.

'You see, we had good instructions from our madame. She taught us how to play around with them, especially to massage the prick and the balls with cleverness, so that the customer was half ready before the real act started. That makes it easier, of course. Most men wanted to be Frenched. Now, when a guy is half ready when you take his tool between your lips, it won't exhaust you.'

'And how did this job end for you?'

'Oh, the madame was tipped off to lay low, so she closed up, went to Florida for her health, and we poor chickens were on our own hook. Mind you, I had saved up more than a thousand dollars, and the other girls were not worse off. I moved to a good hotel and very soon met my present boyfriend. I've been with him already over two years and I'm contented. He is a good man. Of course, I passed as a good girl when I met him, told him a cock-and-bull story, and he still believes it. I think that he'll marry me some day and that's why I'm willing to do anything to have those records destroyed. Will you help me?'

Sarnelli said he would.

She was aware that his prick was blown up again to fine dimensions and she calculated that she was soon going to get what she was after. When his tool was safely placed in her longing cunt and she had him well encircled with her arms and legs, she whispered in his ear:

'Keep still, sweetheart. Keep very still – only for a moment.'

When he complied, she began her party for herself. She twisted and turned under him, pressed and rubbed her love-nest with strong movements against the hair around his shaft, circled and heaved and threw herself up and down so that he had difficulty keeping his balance. She dug her heels into the firm flesh of his behind, her fingers into his shoulders, and finally she came. But she was not selfish. She stretched her legs under him, closed them firmly and made him spread his apart a bit. Her fingers were busy as she answered his fucking movements with rhythmic thrusts. When she felt him coming, she tightened up her pussy as much as possible around his burning love-shaft. They lay quite a while motionless. Then she said:

'You see now why I did not suck you out entirely before. I wanted something for myself and I have it now, don't I?' And with that, she was out of the bed.

It was a tired but satisfied detective who left a respectable young lady after a two-hour visit. Satisfied, also, that she was not connected in any way with the matter under investigation, he had some reflections in his mind about that girl. She certainly was on the borderline. If given a chance, she'd become the respectable wife of a middle-class fellow and probably have kids and a home of her own. But if that man would not take her in for good, she'd be on the bum again pretty soon afterward. Then they would term her a 'fallen woman'. Life was funny.

6

The Altar of Venus

1934

It is curious how much erotica is, or is in the form of, autobiography. *My Secret Life* by 'Walter', Frank Harris's *My Life and Loves*, Sellon's *The Ups and Downs of Life*, *Fanny Hill* by Cleland, 'Lady Harper's' *Queenie*, *Memoirs of Josefine Mutzenbacher* by Salten, *The Romance of Lust* by Potter, Schroeder-Devrient's *Pauline*, *Memoirs of a German Opera Singer*, the whimsical *The Autobiography of a Flea*, and so many more. The reason for this is not hard to fathom. Erotica serves two major functions, to entertain and to educate, and the autobiography form is perfectly suited for both purposes.

It is said that at puberty everyone believes they have discovered something no one else knows about – Sex! The vast library of erotica shows however that since the beginning of recorded history, little has changed in the sexual world. Perhaps technology has added a few new 'toys' to the amatory arsenal, and Nature a few new diseases, but that is all. Even before Freud, Kinsey and Masters & Johnson, humankind was hardly in the dark about most matters of sex. Erotica in all its forms has always provided 'how-to' sex information, as well as a myriad of case-study material, for erotica is in fact the record of the experiences, observations and fantasies of thousands of years of human sexuality. Once the fantasy and reality have been separated it is clear that 'modern' case history simply repeats what has already been recorded in erotic literature.

Today we entrust the field of sexology to medical and para-medical professionals – psychiatrists, psychologists, physiologists, anatomists, sociologists, etc. Yet the pioneers of modern sexological dogma were (no pun intended) lay people. Long before the establishment of psychiatric institutes and university departments, people from all walks of life were making detailed and accurate observations about human sexuality. Some wrote down their findings and theories as academic treatises, others as 'fiction', the latter being more common if the researcher was a non-medical person and wished to avoid any stigmas attached to being known as 'curious' about matters sexual. Very few, though, were brave or honest enough to pen signed, admittedly erotic autobiographies. This sadly led to all erotica being dismissed as fiction, and ignored by scholars as any type of useful information. As a result, the most famous sex experts in history became those authors who were just most successful at getting their thoughts accepted by a large public, irrespective of the merit of their teachings. Their fame in the end was no endorsement of the accuracy of their 'sexual truths' as evidenced by the vast number of myths that have been generated over the centuries and are only now being discredited. To these ranks, for example, belong the Drs Simon André Tissot (*L'Onanism*, 1764) and Nicholas Venette (*Tableau de l'amour . . .* , 1687) whose works on masturbation and conjugal love respectively are still in print and continue to perpetrate wrong sexual information (e.g. masturbation causes blindness, the sex of offspring can be controlled by lying on one's left side during coition, etc.).

A great failure of modern sexual science has been this ignoring of erotica as primary research material. Yale professor Peter Gay's scholarly study of Victorian sexuality, *Education of the Senses*, revealed as false the popular myths of that society's lack of interest in matters sensual and amatory. Yet any reader of Victorian erotica already knew that. It took however the special talents and 'authority' of the academic to separate the fact from the fantasy, and to organise and analyse the facts so they could be scientifically treated and hence gain wide public acceptance.

Scientists aside, one of the most astute and clinical observers of turn-of-the-century sexual behaviour was the anonymous author of *The Altar of Venus*, 'Published exclusively for Members of the Anglo-Esoterical Society, London, England, MCMXXXIV'. Preliminary material in the first printed edition of this book states this work to be the manuscript of an erotic autobiography by a recently deceased member of the House of Lords. Though nothing in the book explains how the narrator, a man born into a middle-class English home in 1900, became a Lord of the Realm before his death some mere thirty years later, the accuracy of the author's observations and theories on the psychology and physiology of human sex from childhood to adulthood cannot be dismissed. This is not just a skilfully conceived novel in the form of an autobiography, this is a work of sexual facts. Starting with his first erotic experimentations at the age of five or six, the author, who calls himself Gilbert in the text, lucidly and unblushingly portrays the variety of sexual activities available during his lifetime, the social settings in which they occurred, and the consequences of his personal indulgences.

From an early age the author showed a keen interest in the hows and whys of sex, and his curiosity was fortunately oriented equally towards both mental and physical aspects. He lived in the time of Freud, Havelock Ellis, Forel, Moll, Hirschfeld, Stekel and the other founders of twentieth-century psycho-sexual science, and their writings must have influenced his thoughts. Yet his style is not at all pedantic, it is rather journalistic, as if he took a diary and turned it into a prose novel.

The Altar of Venus is a unique opportunity to see into the post-Victorian sexual psyche. In ways it is a continuation of the encyclopaedic *My Secret Life* which is now recognised by social scientists to be a wealth of accurate information about the English libido from 1830 to 1890. Fortunately, unlike *My Secret Life* which is matter-of-fact to the extreme, *The Altar of Venus* is as erotically entertaining as it is psycho-sexually illuminating. Though not a scientist by training, the author is empiric in approach, and engages in self-analysis. Gilbert recalls his own theories on such topics as modesty, masturbation, oral sex, prostitution, sado-masochism, erotica, and the psycho-sexual differences between men and women. The author's sexual revelations probably shocked the generation of the 1930s. Despite modern research and our self-proclaimed worldliness, some of what he has to report is still surprising, and only just now being confirmed with facts and figures, especially his recounting of the frequency and sophistication of pubescent and pre-pubescent sexual activity, the amount of incest that occurred around him, and the inherent sadomasochistic yearnings in all age groups.

The selection from *The Altar of Venus* that follows is an episode from late in Gilbert's life, when he kept as a mistress Edyth, a very sexy and emancipated lady of his own age, who has just told the author the strange story of her first marriage.

～ from *The Altar of Venus*

The dramatic effect of Edyth's story was highly intensified by the fact that she was naturally very modest, even bashful – and the scarlet flame which lit her cheeks as certain portions of the narrative obliged her to use obscene words and phrases betrayed the effort it was costing her to repeat the lurid tale.

In her sexual expansions she was the embodiment of passionate fervour. But both before and after the act, an innate modesty cloaked her words and actions. She was easily embarrassed and blushed furiously at anything savouring of naughtiness, and her reluctance and ingenuous confusion at being seen naked was something delicious to behold. I had seen so much boldness and had been so accustomed to having mere nudity taken quite for granted that her blushing bashfulness was really a delightful contrast. I entertained myself by teasing her with the deliberate intention of provoking blushes, begging her to let me see her naked or watch her while she was bathing, enticing her to take curious and unusual postures in intercourse, asking her to tell me how it felt and how many times she had 'come', etc., all of which threw her into the greatest confusion.

I have said that Edyth had no vices or eccentricities. She had, however, one passionate hobby and one peculiar physical characteristic. The physical peculiarity to which I have referred was something of a more intimate nature. She was one of those extremely rare females whom Mother Nature has endowed with what I, not knowing the scientific term, would call a tit-shaped clitoris. In my entire experience I have only encountered them in three women.

Edyth's clitoris, under the influence of erotic stimulation, stiffened out in rigid erection, some three-eighths of an inch or more, and while so erected, the slightest touch upon it was sufficient to throw her into wild frenzy. As orgasm approached, she lost all control of herself and gave such vociferous expression to her feelings as I had never listened to before. Warnings to the effect that she would surely be overheard by occupants of adjoining apartments had no effect whatsoever. In her erotic frenzy nothing existed at the moment but she and I. Her demonstrations heightened my own excitation, but they also embarrassed me, for I knew that they could, in the stillness of the night, be heard all through the building.

Eventually I struck on the idea of placing my hand over her mouth before she reached orgasm. The first time I did this she sputtered and choked and indignantly accused me of trying to strangle her, but I accustomed her to the system. She said it 'spoiled' part of her pleasure and I disliked to do it, but I didn't relish the idea of providing the neighbours with free entertainment nightly and I had observed sly smiles on their faces when we passed them in the halls.

Edyth's naïve modesty and simplicity charmed and intrigued me. With the exception of the drama she had enacted for the purpose of revenging herself on her husband, her sexual experiences had been confined to the most conservative of conjugal expansions. From what she told me I gathered that her husband had not been of a very ardent disposition or else was weak sexually.

'It always took a long time for his thing to get stiff enough to go in!' she confided with a blush.

Their sexual unions had been limited to once a week or less and it was with surprise she found that I could accommodate her every night or, when so inclined, two or three times. Her disappointing married life and the period of complete abstinence which followed it had brought her to a condition in which she was a veritable treasure-house of hoarded emotions, and it was exactly at this propitious moment that I, to my good fortune, entered her life.

Her ideas as to what was proper were quaint in the extreme. Intercourse was supposed to be indulged in only at night and under cover of darkness. To leave the light on or, in fact, even to be seen naked was immodest. The only proper position was that in which the woman lies on her back with the man on top. Mutual handling or caressing of genital organs was very naughty, and as for the refinements and perversions of love to which she had heard allusions of whose exact nature she had but vague ideas, they were not even to be discussed except in whispers.

I took a cynical and wicked delight in exploiting the innocent superstitions as fast as they came to my notice and diverted myself immensely by inciting certain conflicts between her naturally voluptuous disposition and this quaint modesty.

'Edyth, darling,' I pleaded coaxingly, as prior to retiring for the night she slipped on her nightgown before removing her undergarments, 'why don't you want me to see you naked? You know I love to . . . but you always have something on, just to deprive me of the pleasure!'

'Gilbert! You've seen me naked often enough!'

'Why, darling, you know I haven't seen you naked half a dozen times. You've got the prettiest form of any girl I ever saw,' I would add cunningly, 'I don't see why you want to keep it hidden from me.' Such a plea, of course, was irresistible.

'Well, for heaven's sake! I suppose you'll keep on teasing until I take off my nightgown!' And off it came while she stood blushing before me for a moment.

'Come closer, darling.'

When she came within arm's reach, I twined my fingers in the cluster of silky brown curls at the apex of her legs.

'I had a suspicion about what part of my form you wanted to see!'

When I learned that intercourse was supposed to be enjoyed only at night under cover of darkness, I immediately developed an insatiable desire for daylight gratification.

'Edyth,' I whispered one day when I took her on my knees after lunch, 'I want to do it so badly I just can't wait until night. Just feel this!'

'But I'm all dressed!' she exclaimed in a suffocated voice.

'All you have to do is just slip off your panties!' A bit of coaxing, liberally interspersed with kisses, and as usual I won my point. With reddened cheeks, she unfastened the little silken garment and lay down on the sofa.

'Darling, lie face down this time. It gives me the nicest feeling to have your bottom rubbing against me!'

'Gilbert!' she protested in shocked indignation.

In this, as always, she yielded after the requisite coaxing, turning over on her stomach. I raised her dress, exposing the firm beautiful hemispheres, and placed myself above her with my knees between her legs. Slipping one hand down the front of her bodice over one of her breasts, I inserted the other one under her abdomen and placed my finger on her clitoris. Her bottom quivered and vibrated against my stomach in instantaneous response to the caress.

The opportunity to let her make all the racket she wanted to was a good one, for it was midday and the noise of traffic in the street below was such as to lessen the probability of being overheard. Pressing my cock into her vagina as far as it would go, I began to titillate her clitoris with my finger.

'Oh! Oh! Oh!' she shrieked, 'Oh, that's good! It's wonderful! Oh! Gilbert, dearest, darling! Don't stop! Oh! Oh! Oh!'

For ten or fifteen minutes I kept her squealing and kicking under the double provocation of a cock inside and a finger outside, and then unable longer to resist the contagious excitation, my own orgasm released itself.

'Gilbert, did I make much noise?' she asked guiltily after it was all over and we had arranged our clothing.

'If there was anyone closer than Trafalgar Square who didn't hear you, I'll be surprised, darling.'

'Oh!' she gasped, horrified. 'Why didn't you put your hand over my mouth?'

'You know where both my hands were, dear. Tell me, darling, did it feel nice? Do you like it that way? How many times did you come?'

'Gilbert! I don't want to talk about it!'

'Why not, darling?'

'Gilbert, will you please hush up?'

The extreme sensitiveness of her clitoris and its peculiar erectile qualities set me to speculating, almost involuntarily, as to what the effect of a warm tongue on it would be. Out of respect to her, I had refrained from even tentative explorations in the way of 'Frenching', but chance brought up the subject one night.

We were in bed and Edyth was lying cuddled up by me. She was in a talkative mood. She had asked me a number of questions about Paris and my experiences there, to which I gave discreet replies. Snuggling up closer to me, she said: 'Gilbert, there's something I want to ask you about . . . ' She hesitated a moment and continued in a low voice: 'A woman told me but I don't know whether it's really true. Do those French girls really let men do it to them in the mouth? . . . And do men do it to them with their tongues, too?'

When I was able to speak with composure, I replied: 'Well, darling, the French girls haven't any exclusive patents on it! I guess women of all nationalities take it that way sometimes, if they like a man well enough. And the same thing applies to men.'

'Gilbert! Did you ever do that to a woman with your tongue?'

'Who? Me? Why, no, darling,' I answered discreetly, 'I never met a woman I cared for well enough to do that. That is, until I met you. I'd do it that way for you in a minute, if you wanted it.'

'Why, Gilbert! That's terrible!'

'Why is it terrible, honey?'

'It's nasty!'

'That depends on the woman. You're not nasty. You spend half your time in the bathtub. You're as clean and sweet down there as a newly budded rose!'

'I don't mean that way! I mean, it's indecent!'

'Well, darling,' I lied hypocritically, 'I always thought so, too, until I met you. Some way, that sort of makes it seem different. You're so fresh and sweet I'd just as soon put my lips on this (and I placed my hand on it) as I would on your cheek!'

She remained silent for a few moments, digesting what I had said, and I whispered insinuatingly: 'They say it feels wonderful to a woman, better than any other way. Do you want me to do it to you once that way, just to see?'

'Gilbert! Hush up!'

'Just feel how this little thing is swelling up! I'll bet it would like a nice kiss if its mama didn't object!'

Her limbs trembled convulsively and the 'little thing' to which I referred was standing up and pulsing violently.

'Gilbert! . . . If you don't hush up, I swear I'll get up and sleep on the lounge! Take your hand away from there!'

'All right, darling!'

The next day, while leaving a store in which I had purchased some little gifts for her, my attention was attracted to a beautiful coat on display in the window. It was an exquisite garment of genuine ermine, and a price tag announced that it was on sale at the specially reduced price of forty pounds. Business had been good and I was tempted to buy the coat for Edyth. I turned and started back into the store but, as I did so, it occurred to me that perhaps it would be advisable to get her opinion on it before making the rather costly purchase.

After we had dined that night I suggested a walk. Window-shopping was one of her favourite diversions and she agreed with alacrity. A bit later we were gazing into shop windows at finery temptingly displayed, and without disclosing my purpose, I steered her around until we were in front of the store where the coat was on display.

'Look at that coat, Edyth!' I exclaimed. 'Isn't it a beauty?'

She gazed at it rapt-eyed and drew a deep breath. 'Oh! Isn't it lovely! And look, Gilbert, only forty pounds!'

She feasted her eyes on it and, as she reluctantly turned away, I said carefully: 'Well, we'll be rich soon and you'll have a coat like that.'

It was my intention to surprise her with it the next day.

We returned to our apartment and, while I sat in the library, reading the evening paper, Edyth undressed, and soon I heard her splashing in the bathtub. When she finished bathing she came into the room where I was sitting with a dressing gown draped about her and sat down. She seemed to be preoccupied and was silent until I laid down my paper. As I did so, she remarked pensively:

'I sure would like to have that coat we saw.'

'Yes, the coat is a beauty. Looks like it was just made for you.'

'It's a bargain, too. Only forty pounds.'

'We'll be able to buy coats like that before long if business continues to improve.'

'I've got ten pounds saved up now. I believe I could save the rest in three or four months.'

'I'm afraid the coat will be sold long before that, honey.'

I got up and, standing behind her chair, tilted her face upward and kissed her lips. As I did so, the dressing gown fell open sufficiently to disclose a pair of luscious white boobies, free for once of their customary harness. And as pretty breasts always have done, and always will, they turned my thoughts to subjects other than coats.

More with the intention of teasing her than seriously and without premeditation, I said as my hands closed over the snowy globes:

'Honey, you know we're not exactly rich, but I'll make you a proposition. Let me do that to you once and I'll buy you the coat!'

She looked at me uncomprehendingly.

'Do what?' she asked.

'You know . . . what we were talking about last night.'

She gazed at me wide-eyed for a moment and then, as she recollected the subject of our conversation of the previous evening and comprehended what I meant, she turned crimson and exclaimed: 'Gilbert! Stop talking about those indecent French tricks!'

'You'd look marvellous in that coat.'

'Will you hush up?'

'And the price they've got it marked . . . it will be gone before noon tomorrow.'

'No!'

'Just once, to see what it's like?'

'No! No! No!'

And she jumped up and fled into the bedroom. Snickering to myself, I again picked up my paper. A few minutes later she was back again and, as I glanced at her, I saw that her cheeks were still red. She appeared to have something she wished to say and I waited expectantly.

'Gilbert . . . ' she murmured, and hesitated uncertainly.

'Well, honey?'

'Gilbert . . . did you . . . really mean . . . what you said?'

'About what, darling?'

'That if I let you do that to me once, you'd buy me that coat?'

With each word the colour in her face became more vivid.

'Of course I mean it, honey! I wouldn't go back on my word.'

There was a long silence, during which her eyes were turned toward the floor.

'Well . . . all right, then!'

'Hurrah!' I exclaimed. 'I've been wanting to try that so bad I just couldn't hardly wait for you to say yes!' And jumping from my chair, I lifted her up in my arms, kissed her flushed cheeks and then stood her back on the floor.

'Just this once now. Remember that!'

'Well, hurry up then and come to bed and get it over with!'

As she stood there with cheeks blazing and eyes averted, an idea occurred to me by which an additional touch of the exotic might be added to the delicious rite, and without saying anything to her, I immediately began clearing off the big library table. When I had removed its divers ornaments and utilities, I told her to bring a blanket and pillow from the bedroom.

'What for?' she asked in bewilderment.

'For you to lie on, honey. I'm going to put them on the table.'

'On the table?' she gasped.

'Yes, on the table, honey. Just like a big luscious piece of strawberry shortcake. Only this shortcake won't need any cream or sugar!'

'Gilbert!' she exclaimed in a horrified voice.

'With the coat you'll be the prettiest girl in London.'

'Gilbert! I am not going to get up on that table!'

'Genuine ermine, too. The rest of these ladies around here will be green with envy,' I continued, and without waiting for her to execute the order, I went myself to the bedroom and obtained the articles referred to and arranged them on the massive table.

She watched my preparations to serve her up like a plate of after-dinner dessert as though paralysed. I couldn't contain myself, but I managed to keep a straight face and, when all was arranged to my satisfaction, I said: 'All right, honey! Now you can take your clothes off!'

Mechanically, her fingers unfastened the belt of the dressing robe and she removed the garment. Chemise, panties, hose and slippers remained. Without divesting herself of any of these, moving as one in a hypnotic trance, she slowly approached the table.

'Your panties, darling! Aren't you going to take them off? I can't do that while you have them on!'

'Well, for heaven's sake! I can take them off after you turn out the light, can't I?'

'But, darling, I'm not going to put out the light. I couldn't see to do it right in the dark!'

'Gilbert! I'm not going to get on that table naked, with the lights on! I won't do it.'

'Honey, you're the most persistent little "no girl" I ever met in my life. I'll tell you what we can do. I'll turn them all out except just the mantel light.'

I pressed the button which controlled the cluster of lights above the table, extinguishing them, and turned on a shaded globe on one side of the fireplace mantel. It illuminated the room with a soft, pink refulgence.

'All right, sweetheart. Now you can take off your panties and get up on the table.'

'Well, turn around then and don't look at me!'

'I can't see what difference it makes if I look!' But I turned my back obediently. When I looked around again, the panties were off.

Under the tinted, subdued rays of light, her arms and shoulders and such other portions of her bare flesh as were visible glowed rosily. I lifted her up and set her upon the edge of the table, and with the idea of stimulating her sensibilities, I filled a goblet with wine and handed it to her. She drank it and, after disposing of the empty glass, I gently pushed her down on her back with her knees over the edge of the table.

These preliminaries were, of course, affording me the most delicious thrills imaginable. In all my experience I had never 'Frenched' a girl under more inciting circumstances. My cock was in a state which threatened the integrity of the buttons of my trousers and the first thing I did after I got her stretched out on the table was to unfasten them and allow it its freedom.

I leaned over her and slipped up the silk underwaist she had pulled down over her thighs. Her limbs quivered as I raised it and she placed an arm over her eyes. I worked the diaphanous garment upward until her breasts were completely exposed in the rosy light. With this detail complete, I drew up a chair and, placing it close to the table, sat down.

True to form, when she had lain down on the table, she had clenched her legs together as tightly as she could – but I let this pass for the moment and contented myself with caressing her legs, hips, thighs and breasts with my hands. Then, pressing my lips to one of her legs, just above the top of her stocking, and dropping kisses along the route, I began an upward journey. Her limbs twitched and quivered as though each kiss were an electric shock. When my lips reached the place where a dark triangle of curly hair marked the juncture of her thighs, I hitched the chair a little closer and, placing my hands on her knees, endeavoured to separate them. At first they seemed disinclined to part, so I applied a little more force and gradually, as I continued to urge them with a firm pressure, they began to yield.

And now, under the rose-tinted light, my little sweetheart's sexual flower, with its border of dark chestnut curls, was revealed. I separated the moist lips and the little tit-shaped protuberance in their upper extremity, which my fingers had often caressed but my eyes never before contemplated, came into view. This was the naughty little thing which caused her to moan and squeal and go into hysterical fits whenever it was petted, and I gazed at it curiously. And even as I looked, it began to expand perceptibly in size, as though excited at merely being viewed. It stiffened out and then shrank back slightly, repeating the process at intervals of a few seconds. I placed my fingertip upon it. It was hard and firm and pulsated vigorously to my touch.

'Are you deliberately trying to drive me crazy?' she exclaimed in a tense, indignant whisper. 'Well, for heaven's sake! How much longer are you going to look?'

'Lie down, sweetheart. I won't look any more if you don't want me to!'

She lay down again, still murmuring indignant protests, and an instant later my face was between her thighs. Up and down the length of the humid cleft my tongue scurried and finally settled down to work in earnest on her clitoris. It rose valiantly to meet the attack and projected itself outward. And then pandemonium broke loose.

Grimly I stayed at the post – indifferent for once as to whether the neighbours might think I was slaughtering her and break in the door or called the police. Between her writhing, twisting and kicking, it was all I could do to keep my tongue on the right spot. Part of the time her legs were sticking straight out on either side of me – part of the time they were flying up and down in a fantastic dance – and part of the time they were clasped about my neck. She raised herself on her wrists, she dropped back and tried to elevate her bottom, she twisted and wriggled until I was obliged to seize her by the hips to hold her still. No adequate reproduction of the shrieks, moans and exclamations with which she emphasised her frenzy is possible.

How many times she had orgasm I couldn't determine, but the nectar of love was dripping within a minute or so after I had first gotten my mouth on her. Finally, I felt her body relax. She put her hands on my head and gasped: 'I can't stand any more, Gilbert!'

The performance had produced such a tension in my own nerves that I was not far from spontaneous ejaculation. Under the pressure of her hands on my forehead, I reluctantly yielded my position. Sliding the chair back, I got up, went to the bathroom, brought a moistened towel and sponged her thighs. It was the first time I had ever performed such an intimate service for her, but she was too exhausted to protest. Picking her up in my arms, I carried her to our sleeping quarters, laid her down on the bed and sat down on the edge by her side.

A bit later we were cuddled up in each other's arms in bed.

'Gilbert . . . you don't have to buy me that coat. And . . . and . . . '

'And what, darling?'

'If you like to do that . . . you can do it again . . . sometime!'

'When?'

'Oh, when you want to! Tomorrow, if you like!'

'That's a bargain, you little old sweet thing! Tell me, honey, how did it feel?'

'Hush up!'

'But, darling, after going to all that trouble just to find out?'

'Well, what do you want to know?'

'I just want to know whether it felt nice.'

'Yes! Yes!'

'Better than the other way?'

'No . . . yes . . . Oh, I don't know! Now will you stop talking about it?'

Needless to say, she got the coat. And from that time on I enjoyed numerous special after-dinner desserts on the big library table.

One day, not long after her first surrender to cunnilingus, a matter came up which obliged me to make a business trip to a nearby city. As the weather was pleasant, it occurred to me to take her with me. It was a four-hour drive so I rented a car and chauffeur for the day.

The business being satisfactorily concluded by mid-afternoon, we had dinner in a local restaurant and started back home in the evening. After an hour on the road, Edyth, who had gotten up earlier that morning than was her custom, nestled against me and went to sleep.

The position in which she had placed herself brought her cheek in close contact with a certain portion of my trousers where ordinarily a little extra allowance is made in the cloth for something beside leg. This something, always responsive to the slightest attention and easily awakened, answered the warmth and pressure of her cheek by increasing rapidly in size. And as the pressure was not removed, it continued to expand until it reached the limit of its expansional capacity, and thereafter gave evidence of its appreciation by a series of throbs and muscular contractions.

I supposed that Edyth was now fast asleep but in this I was somewhat mistaken, for before long she stirred again. This time she raised her head slightly, her hand moved up and her fingers began unfastening the buttons on the front of my trousers. Her hand slipped inside and after a bit of fumbling with interior garments came out with something warm, stiff and rigid clasped in her fingers. She adjusted the blanket so that it entirely covered her head and lay down again, this time with my naked cock under her soft cheek.

I reached over and snapped off the small electric light which illuminated the interior of the car, and sat quietly with my cock throbbing between the constriction of her cheek and my own leg. Had she been one of the many women I had associated with previously, there would not have been anything in this to surprise me, but Edyth, despite the fact that she always yielded to my coaxing, never herself took the lead in any of our little adventures in concupiscence. Her present action was, therefore, quite out of the ordinary. However, I was destined for a still greater surprise.

She moved again, releasing the prisoner from beneath her face. But its freedom was only temporary and to my amazement, I suddenly felt a pair of warm lips close about it. I sat perfectly still. The lips remained motionless for a moment and then advanced, so that a considerably larger portion of my cock was within their embrace. Another short interval of inactivity and then I perceived the pull of strong, vigorous suction and the action of a hot little tongue playing over the head. So energetic and determined was the caress, that in sixty seconds or less, my testicles were threatening to release their hoard. I placed my hand on her head to ease her away until I could again get control of the situation. But instead of surrendering the audacious thing, she pushed my hand away and sucked still harder, and before I could avoid it, the seminal reservoirs were emptying their contents into her mouth.

When I finally got free of her, I hastily handed her a handkerchief and whispered: 'Spit it out, sweetheart!'

'I can't!' she gasped, 'it went down my throat!'

'All right, all right!' I replied, hurriedly. 'It won't hurt you!'

And I lifted her up in my arms and set her down very gently on my lap.

I slipped my hand up under her dress and inside her panties. As I had divined, her genitals were dripping wet, and her clitoris standing up rigidly. She trembled as my fingers came in contact with it, placed her hand over mine, squeezed it tightly for a moment between her thighs and then gently withdrew it.

'Wait until we get home, Gilbert!' she whispered.

And the low but vibrant words augured an enjoyable termination to the adventure later.

7

Two Flappers in Paris
*c.*1934

One does not usually associate the words 'charming', 'sweet' or 'cute' with books that have been labelled hard-core pornography. Yet these words come to mind after first reading *Two Flappers in Paris*. The likely explanation is that this erotic novel from the 1930s does not, and never did, deserve the pejorative label it has received. Sexually explicit stories need not be crude, coarse, gutter trash (although many are), and *Two Flappers in Paris* proves this point.

Two Flappers in Paris is a bibliographic enigma. The author's name, 'A. Cantab' is certainly a pseudonym, as 'cantab' is English slang for a Cambridge University student. (In the US, 'cantab' refers to a student of Harvard University, which is located in Cambridge, Massachusetts.) Only a single bibliography of erotic books lists this title, Alfred Rose's 1936 *Registrum Librorum Eroticorum* (which is principally a shelf list of the erotic books in the British Library's secret and restricted Private Case collection). However there is no indication that there was ever actually a copy of this title in the Private Case, for unlike with other books listed in his bibliography, Rose gave no press mark for this book, and Kearney's 1981 *Private Case: An Annotated Bibliography* showed no copy present at that time. No mention of *Two Flappers in Paris* is made in C. R. Dawes's unpublished manuscript study of English erotic books, which is quite complete up to 1933. Apparently Rose had independent, personal knowledge of this book, which must have appeared between 1933 and 1936. His description of the book, as item 4601 in his two-volume bibliography, indicated it to be '140 pages, crown octavo in size, Printed for Subscribers Only, London–Paris, no date'. No copy of this edition is known to exist. The earliest edition available for examination is 127 pages, and published by 'The Erotica Biblion Society of London–New York'. Once again no date given. This particular edition, based on typography and physical construction, seems to have been printed in Paris, *c.*1935. 'The Erotica Biblion Society' as an imprint was first seen at the end of the nineteenth century, when H. S. Nichols and Leonard Smithers used it as a cover for erotica they published. The notorious Paris publisher Charles Carrington (died 1922) used this imprint for some of his erotica, and it is very likely that the imprint was further used by his two assistants, and successors, Groves and Micheaux, who were active in the Paris book world in the 1930s. (Almost simultaneously with the Paris edition, there appeared an American edition in New York City, one hundred and twenty pages with five crude woodcuts, and the imprint 'The Erotica Biblion Society'. Curiously, H. S. Nichols, who had fled Europe in the early years of the twentieth century, was in New York at that time!)

What of the novel itself? The protagonist, Jack W—, is a somewhat senior British Diplomat, who, on his way to the British Embassy in Paris, meets an attractive younger Englishwoman, Evelyn H—, who is herself on the way to a boarding school in Paris, where she is to meet her best friend, Nora A—. (The author is most certainly English, as British slang, e.g. 'waterproof' for raincoat, and British spellings, e.g. 'favourite', are used throughout the story.) The ferry ride from Folkestone to Calais is very rough, and the two pass the time in conversation. When Jack turns the topic to art, then nudes, and then artistic portrayal of the 'male member', he discovers Evelyn to be quite embarrassed, as she has been, he learns, extremely sheltered in her upbringing and is still a virgin! Pressing the subject further, he finds Evelyn to also be very curious about sexual matters, and eager to learn all about the 'secret mysteries of life' she has heard her friends whisper and giggle about. The diplomat sees an opportunity too good to pass up. He arranges to meet Evelyn and her friend Nora in a few days , after he has had time to settle into his new position, and he promises to provide an education the two young women never got at school.

True to his word, Jack escorts Evelyn and her friend out for the afternoon, as if they are only going for a pleasant day at the amusement park. However, it is very adult amusement that is desired as the three travel to a most exclusive brothel where the diplomat has already arranged with the madame his guests' sex education. Orchestrated as a six-course curriculum, the curious girls quickly progress from one station to the next. With 'Ohs!' and 'Ahs!' and coy, affected maidenly protests, the eager pupils see stag films and live sex shows, and speak with the 'actresses', who then continue with the 'hands on' part of the young ladies' education, demonstrating techniques of sexual excitation, using a very willing 'uncle' Jack as the model for a lesson on male anatomy. Evelyn and Nora receive instruction and first-hand experience in the pleasures afforded by the brothel's various specially equipped rooms, including the whipping room. The girls are apt, willing and appreciative students.

It is easy to see how such a storyline could be developed as a smutty book of orgiastic riot and unbridled depravity, with sweaty, lust-driven bodies grasping frantically for the next new thrill and orgasmic release. *Two Flappers in Paris* is not this at all. Throughout the novel, the atmosphere of civility and gentility is never lost, not even in the heat of deepest passion. Perhaps this is because it has been decided in advance that the pupils' virginities are to remain intact (less of a problem than one might think, as the reader soon discovers). More so it is because this is 'A. Cantab's' style, and what gives *Two Flappers in Paris* its special flavour.

Two Flappers in Paris is a basically uncomplicated, simple story. It mostly occurs in the space of a single afternoon, and is told in real time. No flashbacks, no plot twists, no psychology or psychoanalysis of the characters' actions and motives. Sex action, not character development is the focus of the book. It is perhaps more a novella than novel in construction, but who cares? The girls start as delightful, naïve, innocents, and finish as sexually educated, but no more emotionally mature young ladies. Their charm and gleeful curiosity are unchanged. The novel is amoral – education is a virtue for its own sake, and the sexual nature of the instruction is a *non sequitur*. Some may interpret the carefree, gay, unconcerned, fun-oriented attitude of the characters as a mirror of their times, for such was the mien of the 'Flapper Age', that period of history from the end of World War I in 1918 until the Great Depression of 1929. Here was a period when the fetters and deprivations of four years of world conflagration were put out of mind with a nonstop party, fuelled by an ever upward stock market, dwindling class distinction, eternal optimism, and boundless enthusiasm. The frenetic energy of the Charleston well symbolised this age, as did the devil-may-care behaviour of the newly enfranchised, 'liberated' women, the flappers, with their cigarette in hand and the ever rising hemlines of their tassel-fringed skirts. The victorious citizenry of the war to end all wars weren't interested in defining or enforcing any morality, their celebration disregarded encumbrances on their personal activities, especially Prohibition where it existed. It was a time much like our own, but without the fear of sexually transmitted plagues. Sex was fun, and an end unto itself, and such is the attitude of this novel of that time.

Here then is an excerpt from *Two Flappers in Paris*, in which Rose, an employee of the brothel, demonstrates all in the fun to be had with a device called 'The Chair of Pleasure'.

from *Two Flappers in Paris*

The girls were back in a few minutes looking as bright and fresh as ever, and Rose at once led us into the room in which is the 'Chair of Pleasure'. This chair is a kind of armchair with a rather narrow seat and a padded back. On each side, instead of arms, are supports, also padded, on which the legs of the occupant can be comfortably hung. The height of the seat can be regulated at pleasure: So, too, the back can be sloped backwards and, when the legs of the 'subject' are placed on the supports, these can be opened at will, thus separating the thighs.

Facing the chair, and fastened to the front legs by a kind of socket, is a sort of Saint Andrew's cross, an X, provided in the middle part of the lower arms with padded supports for the knees of the 'operator'. This X can be sloped forwards.

The effect of the arrangement can be at once understood: When the girl is seated with her legs raised and well separated the man kneels down on the X, which slopes forward and brings his mouth into most convenient position for dealing with the treasures displayed before him. At the same time, a second girl, lying under the chair, with her head between the lower arms of the X, finds herself admirably placed for an attack with lips and hands on the central regions of his body.

Rose explained to us in detail the utility of the apparatus. 'But,' said Rose in conclusion, 'no explanation is anything like really experiencing what I have been describing. Which of the young ladies will first take her place on the chair?'

'Nora must!' decided Evelyn. 'But I will take her place afterwards, for I want to know everything! Oh! Uncle Jack! How exciting it all is and how delightful to know about all these things.'

'You are not shocked, Evelyn?'

'Of course not! Why should I be? I know that these things are not for little girls, but I am aware also that women know all about them. So nothing shocks me. And, besides, it doesn't prevent us from being modest, does it?'

'Certainly not, Evelyn. And when you and Nora are as learned as the most experienced women, it doesn't follow that you need give yourselves to the first comer, eh?'

'Oh, no indeed,' said Nora with comic dignity. 'I'm sure we shall be most discerning and particular!'

Rose laughed heartily at this, and, as I was gently urging Nora toward the chair in my impatience to enjoy her charms, she took me by the arm.

'One moment,' she said. 'If Miss Nora is wise, she will make herself quite comfortable before sitting down on the chair. There is nothing so tiresome as finding one's clothes in the way!'

At these words, Nora turned toward me blushing delightfully, and I could see that a shy fit had come over her.

'Nora, darling!' I said, pressing her softly in my arms. 'What is it? What's the matter?'

'Oh, Uncle Jack!' she said 'What does it mean? Does it mean that I am to undress?'

'Yes, of course, darling. That's just what Rose means. And, indeed, it's quite necessary. It's always done, you know. It's one of the things that you have to learn and I was waiting for Rose to teach you.'

'Take off my clothes!' she murmured. 'Oh, no! Really, I couldn't!'

'Why not? After all, that – '

'Uncle Jack,' broke in Evelyn, 'I understand Nora. Really, she can't take off her clothes!'

'How absurd,' said Rose, rather vexed. 'Why? You both of you had your petticoats up and your drawers down a few minutes ago, and the neighbouring regions fully exposed!'

'Oh, it's not that!' said Evelyn impatiently. 'I mean that Nora can't undress herself. She would never dare to, the little darling. I know her! Somebody will have to do it for her.'

'Shall I?' I suggested. 'Nora, dear, shall I act as your maid?'

She pressed herself softly against me, covered with confusion and yielding herself to my embrace. She was that delightful combination of chastity and desire which, after all, is the breath of life!

'One word?' I begged. 'Say yes, little sweetheart.'

'Ye . . . es,' she whispered in my ear.

Delighted at having to carry out this charming task, I sat down on a chair and drew Nora between my knees as if she had been a little child. In spite of all she had been through, she was still extremely shy and bashful.

She would submit to anything but would not undertake anything on her own. Rose understood perfectly this frame of mind and did not ridicule it . . . girls always understand one another.

Nora covered her face with her hands and I set to work. I unfastened her bodice and gently removed it. At once I was aware of the delightful *odour di femina*, which almost intoxicated me. Under the bodice, the pretty little camisole with its dainty ribbons disclosed the upper part of the back, breasts and arms. The fair nest of the armpits appeared to me, and I could feel the snow-white breasts quiver under the edge of the richly laced chemise.

Having unfastened the skirt and slipped it down to her feet, the emotion I felt was most intense and delicate, and was increased by the fall of the soft petticoat, which disclosed the splendid bottom enclosed in the pretty drawers that I have already described.

To be sure, I had already seen this beautiful bottom, but to uncover it thus by degrees and with my own hands was an additional pleasure.

I unbuttoned the drawers and slipped them down to her feet. Standing as she was, between my legs with her back toward me, the splendid great twin globes almost pressed against my breast. The subtle perfume, formed of the natural odour and the scents which had been used in her ablutions, met my nostrils and increased my desire. I gently turned her toward me and, resting my hands on her bottom, which enabled me to feel, even through the thin chemise, its softness and its firm elasticity, I pressed the sweet child to me.

'You are not afraid, my lovely one, are you?' I whispered. 'You know how much I already love and respect you?'

What a poor, sweet, fluttering thing she was in my hands as I heard her murmur: 'Yes . . . Uncle Jack!'

I seized the lower part of her corset to undo the fastenings, and my fingers felt the soft and exciting warmth of her immaculate belly. I removed the corset after having unfastened the suspenders to which the stockings were attached. In addition to these suspenders, she was wearing a lovely pair of dark blue ribbon garters, trimmed with loops of rose.

I decided to let her keep her stockings and shoes. A flapper, naked but for stockings and shoes, has always been my special delight.

I almost tore off the camisole and chemise, so eager was I to admire the marvels which I knew must be revealed – and, indeed, I was not disappointed. Nora, stripped naked, was worthy of the chisel of a sculptor. Just a nice height, beautifully pink and white, just sufficiently plump, without being too much so, she was made to perfection.

Her breasts were two sweet little hills of snow, each tipped by a rosy nipple. Her supple waist grew smaller in harmony with her broad hips and her beautifully sloping loins, while her full and rounded thighs made one long to feel their pressure. One would have loved to die smothered by their soft but powerful grip.

Resting my hands on Nora's hips I turned her round so that I might enjoy the back view. Here, too, all was perfection. Her lovely rear was marked by dimples which seemed to invite one's kisses, and the well-developed globes stood out bold and exciting, as though offering themselves to the most wanton caress.

'Sit down, sweetie!' I said, hardly able to speak, so intense was my emotion.

She obeyed. Her beautiful blue eyes, so tender and trusting, and slightly swimming as the result of her nervousness, gazed fondly into mine.

I bent over her and for a long moment I glued my lips to hers. As I pressed her naked body to me, she made not the slightest effort to resist my hot embrace.

Then I took her dear legs and placed them in turn over the supports, where they hung quite comfortably. This done, I proceeded to strip, excusing myself to Evelyn and Rose.

In a moment I was absolutely naked, and I must confess that if Evelyn and Nora examined me with excited curiosity, they raised not the slightest objection to the decidedly indecent appearance which I now presented, for my tool was standing as I think it had never stood before. I knelt down on the padded supports of the lower arms of the X and, leaning forward, moved toward her admirably displayed charms.

It is hardly necessary for me to enlarge on my own feelings at this moment, and especially on my sensual emotions; the reader will easily imagine them. It is not often that one finds oneself in the position that I now occupied, my face between the well-opened thighs of a virgin, my eyes and lips within a few inches of her flower, so pure, so fresh, so tempting and so fragrant, and about to make her for the first time acquainted with the delights of a skilful gamahuche!

Placed as she was, Nora presented to me not only her anterior charms, but I was also able to admire and handle her beautiful bottom, the greater part of which protruded beyond the narrow seat of the chair. When Nora found my head advancing between her thighs, she made a little movement as though to withdraw her deliciously rounded bottom.

'Little darling,' I murmured, 'don't be afraid!' I approached my lips to her pouting cunny and began by covering it and its surroundings with warm kisses.

So lovingly did I apply them, they raised floods of pleasure in the very marrow of her being. There was soon evidence of this. Red and swollen like a delightful cherry, the button which serves as the thermometer of feminine pleasure emerged from its grotto. I could not help taking it softly in my lips and sucking it as if it were a delicious bonbon, tickling it keenly with my quick, pointed tongue.

At once, a perfect frenzy of delight seemed to take possession of Nora.

With her hands gripping the sides of the chair, her breasts quivering with the most intense emotion, her belly undulating with the spasms of the approaching love-fit, she stretched herself out on the chair and, in my hands, which had not ceased to caress and fondle them, I felt the cheeks of her bottom begin to quiver and then to stiffen and stiffen till they were as hard as the muscles of a wrestler at the moment of his supreme effort.

Thanks to the position of her head, which was resting on the back of the chair, I was able to watch her lovely face while continuing my caresses. Her lips were open and contracted by the voluptuous agony she was experiencing; her half-closed eyes seemed to turn up to heaven, as if she were about to swoon away, and inarticulate words tumbled forth.

'Oh! Ooooh! Go on! Oh, it's delicious! Oh! I must . . . Oh! Aaaah! Go on! Go on! Oh! I shall die!'

She pressed herself with all her strength against my lips. Sometimes, as the result of her movements, my chin was buried between the powerful cheeks of her bottom in a way that almost drove me mad with desire. Slowly, and using all my skill, I tickled with the tip of my hot moist tongue the delicious little button which I was pressing between my lips, and I was extracting sobs of pleasure and sighs of delight from my little darling when, suddenly, a great shudder of emotion shook me from head to foot.

A new source of pleasure, more distinctly personal, had just been communicated to me. In a moment I realised what it was. Following the instructions of Rose, who had placed some cushions conveniently for her, Evelyn was lying under me in such a position that her face was just on a level with my still-standing prick. And there, somewhat timidly at first, she was caressing my balls, my tool, my bottom and my thighs while her lips softly kissed the red head of my throbbing weapon.

Kneeling by her side, Rose was minutely directing operations. She was showing her how pleasant and effective it is gently to tickle the bottom and just underneath the balls, and was teaching her to roll them delicately in her soft little hands, to frig my prick with one hand while she tickled me with the other, and, finally, to kiss my balls and prick, and to pass her tongue round and round the red head and, with the tip, to tickle the supersensitive little thread which joins the foreskin to the glans.

I was able to feel delightfully how perfectly Evelyn carried out all her instructions, while all the time I continued to suck Nora's little rosebud and to cover her charms with my fondest attentions.

I knew that Rose was coming to the end of her lesson when I felt the head of my prick pressed and sucked by two hot little lips, while a slippery tongue played up and down and all round it. At the same time, two hands continued to fondle and stroke my balls and bottom.

The sensation almost made me spend at once. It was only by the exercise of the utmost restraint that I avoided doing so, and this because I was determined to reserve myself for what I felt sure was to come afterwards. Meanwhile, Nora, who had not the same reasons for restraining herself, had fairly let herself go. To use the words of the Psalms, 'Her soul melted within her.' For the third time that afternoon, her love-sluices were opened and she poured into my delighted lips a copious draught of the essence of her being. For a few moments she lay panting and quivering, her soft white belly undulating with the gradually subsiding spasms.

I, with my eyes closed and my cheek resting on Nora's fair downy bush, abandoned myself to Evelyn's maddening caresses, but with the intention of stopping just short of climax. I was therefore not sorry when, at a sign from Rose, she ceased her ministrations and rose to her feet. I took her in my arms.

'Oh, Evelyn, you darling!' I murmured. 'What don't I owe you for the delightful time you have been giving me?'

'Well,' said Rose. 'You can repay her in kind! And Miss Nora will return the compliment which you have been paying her! That's only fair, isn't it?'

'Quite fair!'

'Undress Miss Evelyn then, and I'm sure you won't find the task in the slightest measure unpleasant!'

I began to laugh and, drawing Evelyn between my knees as I had done in the case of Nora, I asked her: 'May I, darling?'

She smiled shyly at me and whispered, 'Yes, Uncle Jack!'

How sweet and lovely she was! My hands trembled as they unfastened her bodice and then the waist of her skirt, which I removed as well as her petticoat, and again I experienced the sensual pleasure which the sight of a pretty girl in corset and drawers always rouses in me.

Stripping Evelyn was an absolute delight to me. When she was quite naked, as I carried my mind back to our meeting on the boat and then thought what she was to me at this moment, I felt a strong desire to kneel before her and kiss in adoration her feet, her knees, her thighs and the whole of her fresh young body, so full of mystery and so radiant with virgin charm.

And did so.

She hardly defended herself and was happy, in reality, at receiving a homage which she knew to be fully deserved.

My lips wandered over her beautiful body, arousing little quivers of pleasure wherever they passed, and I would have continued the delightful sport if Rose had not interrupted me, saying: 'Come now! Get to work. You will be able to kiss her more conveniently in a moment!'

I myself placed Evelyn on the chair. I placed her legs on the arms, which Rose opened wide apart, and I knelt down on the X, which at once moved toward her.

Beautiful as Nora is, Evelyn is not one whit less so. She is not quite so well built, and is less white, but her skin is as fine, and, if her limbs are less plump, they are more graceful and more full of nerves, which makes them equally alluring. To sum up, when I am with Nora, I think that no one can equal her in beauty and attraction. When I am with Evelyn, I no longer think of Nora, and I find the dark and dazzling Evelyn the most intoxicating of creatures.

Someday, perhaps, I will describe their essential differences more accurately, but now I will content myself with saying that Evelyn is all energy and activity, while at the same time being just as passionately voluptuous as Nora, who, for her part, would rather be passive and tenderly submissive to refined caresses.

For the moment, I was in adoration before Evelyn's sanctuary of love.

A fine, thick, dark brown bush, as curly and soft as astrakhan, sheltered in its shady folds the fountain at which I was about to quench my greedy thirst.

The whole lovely body of the charming girl was quivering with desire. I kissed her thighs and belly and then my active tongue sought out and roused from its grotto the fresh little rosy god who issued forth swollen and delicious, and allowed himself to be seized by my eager lips.

My hands fondled and pressed her thighs and marble bottom, while my tongue softly tickled the little sensitive button.

Evelyn raised herself on the arms of the chair into almost an upright position: Her powerful thighs gripped my cheeks and held me prisoner in their fond embrace. She threw her head back, her neck was arched, and from her half-opened mouth, a very nest for kisses, issued hot exclamations and sobs and sighs of pleasure. Then the sweet child uttered a cry of delight as her fountains were opened and a stream of the dew of love was poured into my eager mouth, for she had locked her thighs round my neck and was pressing her little cunt to my lips in a way which almost smothered me.

The mere memory of this, the first love grip that she ever gave me, almost drives me mad! Evelyn had come much more quickly than Nora. This is always the case with dark girls, so Rose assured me, and my experience agrees with her.

Meanwhile, I was aware that Nora had not been carrying out her part of the programme as Evelyn – who was now lying back in the chair, resting comfortably – had done, and I asked Rose to give her the necessary instructions. Nora lay down under me and, in a moment, I felt her hands stroking me and her lips and tongue sucking and tickling me delightfully. It was perfectly plain to me that she was doing her level best to make me spend again and it was with the utmost difficulty that I restrained myself from pouring a torrent of the seed of life into her hot, juicy little mouth. The moment came when I could resist no more and, jerking my throbbing tool from between her lips, I stood up, panting violently. Nora also got up and looked at me with distress.

'Was I hurting, uncle, dear?' she asked softly.

Great tears were actually gleaming in her beautiful eyes. I took her naked body in my arms and pressed her madly to me, and, as I did so, the pressure of my prick against her soft belly made her tremble with passion and again almost caused me to give way.

'Hurt me, darling!' I said in transport. 'How could you hurt me, my sweet, my love? No, far from it . . . But let me explain.'

I drew Evelyn to me also and made them sit on my knees, and the sensation of the soft, naked bottoms of these two delightful flappers on my thighs was such as I can hardly describe.

'Both of you urge me by your loving caresses to spend just as both of you have just spent, but I don't want to do it again yet.'

'Why?' they both asked together.

'Because, you dears, a man's prick has neither the strength nor the staying power of your little cunnies. When a man spends, he shoots out a stream of love juice, as you know, don't you?'

'Yes, Uncle Jack.'

'Well! Each time that he shoots it out, it is very exhausting for him, and when he has done it three or four times, and not many men can do this, his prick becomes small, quite small, and it is no easy matter to rouse it!'

'But, Uncle Jack,' said Evelyn, laughing. 'You have only . . . spent once and here is your . . . your . . . prick getting quite, quite small, as you say!'

'Oh, what a pity!' exclaimed Nora sadly. 'What is to be done? I should so like to see you come again.'

I must confess that I was highly amused to see how well the two girls remembered the lesson that Rose had given them, but it is my experience that this is always so once a girl has been very well gamahuched by a man and has had his tool in her mouth.

~ 8 ~

Memoirs of a Girl Student

1934

The American college co-ed has been a sexual icon for well over one hundred years. And with good historical precedent. For thousands of years male-dominated society had prohibited the equal education of the sexes. By allowing women only enough schooling to manage simple matters of home and child care, patriarchal society kept females economically and socially dependent on their male relatives. This allowed men to control the minds and bodies (and hence the sexuality) of these *de facto* indentured slaves. The fear was that 'too much' learning would give women 'ideas' and the desire for independence and equality. Moral double standards would crumble and society would be irrevocably altered. The fears were well founded.

Boys and girls were, for the most part, educated in segregated classes until the end of the eighteenth century. Few girls received instruction beyond elementary school in this country until after the Civil War, when pre-college education became increasingly co-educational. The Troy Female Seminary (1821) and Mt Holyoke Seminary (1837) were among the first in the United States to offer women instruction equivalent to male high school and college courses. The same decade saw the first truly co-educational college, Oberlin in Ohio. By the beginning of World War II, most American institutions of higher learning had female students, 'co-eds' (a purely American colloquial contraction for 'co-educational student').

With higher education came the feared emancipation of women, especially after World War I. On campus, out of parental sight and control, young women were free to exercise and indulge their intellectual and physical curiosities, unfetter their libidos and experiment with the then universal symbols of independent adulthood – alcohol, tobacco, drugs and sex. These 'vices' were an accepted part of the college scene, what with Prohibition at an end and the close proximity of so many young men just at their sexual prime. The sophisticated and now worldly flappers of the twenties and their sisters who followed had millennia of repression to make up for, and they did.

Memoirs of a Girl Student, 'Paris, France, 1934', is in fact an original American novel. It is a female counterpart to the famous *The Alter of Venus*, and from the same year. This is neither an autobiography nor even a biography of anyone real, but is obviously 'taken from life'. The still anonymous author, almost certainly a man, states that the book was written on a dare and for money. The subject is simply one girl's experience of sexual education at home and away at school. The setting is California in the 1930s. The language is rich with the colourful slang of the time, when things were 'keen' and 'swell', 'stepping out' was entertainment, an 'ice box' really required ice to keep it cold, and the living room 'davenport' was as acceptable a substitute for a bed as was the back seat of a 'roadster'.

This novel has the easy narrative pace and simple conversational tone of typical Depression Era popular pulp fiction. It also has a rather uncharacteristic but prophetic, xenophobic attitude toward the US's Japanese population. Individual scenes have the feel of a cinema screenplay. This may well be the case, as many Hollywood screenwriters of the time, such as Gene Fowler, Bernard Wolfe, Val Lewton and Lupton Wilkinson, were known to supplement their income with erotic manuscripts. (Part of this story is told in Milton Luboviski's epilogue to the Grove Press edition of 'Henry Miller's' *Opus Pistorum*.) To this day, scriptwriters trying to break into television and film still travel this time-honoured alternate path.

The protagonist, 'Mike' as she chooses to call herself, lives up to the reputation of the co-ed as a loose, liberal, sexually free and emancipated young woman, out for a good time as ardently as her male classmates. Imagine the Hardy Boys and Nancy Drew 'high' on booze and Spanish Fly, forget the mystery, and you have the picture. Throw in a college prostitution ring and some frat house orgies for good measure, and you'll get an education you won't soon forget. Here then is an excerpt from this classic erotica.

◆~◆ from *Memoirs of a Girl Student*

It was several weeks, however, before Edna told Mary and I that if we wanted, she would come over my house again. My father was out of town, and my stepmother was going away the next day, so I told Edna to come over the next afternoon and stay with us all night. She said that she would.

You may imagine that Mary and myself were both crazy for the next night to come. We knew that we would learn more about the question of sex.

Finally the time arrived, and with it our Edna, all smiles and laughter. 'Well, Mike,' she said, addressing me as she kissed me, 'I got well fucked last night, and am eager to tell you both about it. Believe me, it is keen to have a boy's big prick stuck way into your belly.'

I was thrilled through and through at her smutty words, and once in the house I threw my arms around this pretty girl and ran my hand up to her cunt. My other hand went under my own dresses, as my own cunt was itching and twitching. I longed to have it cooled by one of my companion's hands.

Edna took mercy on me and, raising my dresses, she rubbed me on my spot and I was soon a little better. Without the loss of time we hurried to my room, and soon the three of us had all our clothes off and were stark naked. Running to the bed, we hopped in, and as we lay on the bed fondling each other, Edna told us her story. As near as I can remember now, after all this time, it was as follows:

I will tell it all to you from the beginning so that you will both understand just how it all came about. The other day, after I had left school, I met this boy who had made advances to me. He asked me if I wanted to take a walk down through the riverbed in back of his house.

Of course I felt sure that I knew what he was after, and was perfectly willing to go with him. After putting on a little bashful act about going alone down there with him, I, of course, consented.

Sure enough, as soon as we got down in the riverbed and down under the trees where we were out of the sight of any spectators, he began to get familiar with me. He stopped and said, 'Let us stay here a while.' I stopped and looked at him. He came up close to me and, putting his arms around me, pressed his lips to mine in a long, clinging kiss.

Oh, girls, if you only knew how I felt when he kissed me. It sent such thrills of bliss running up and down my spine and seemed to set me on fire, but I just closed my eyes and let him kiss away. I lay against him and he squeezed me. Putting one of his hands on the front of my waist, he squeezed and pressed my breasts, tickling the little tips till I thought I would go mad.

Then he dropped his hand and I felt it on my leg. He rubbed and squeezed me, then raised up my dress. When he found that I had on a pair of tight bloomers, he made a vile remark, withdrew his hand and pushed me away.

I was very sorry that he had taken his hand away, as I was feeling real good, and you may be sure, girls, that that is the very last time that I will ever wear bloomers, for I know a whole lot better. From now on I am going to be open for the boys, and will wear nothing but teddies to avoid any complications.

We were standing right in front of a clump of trees with a nice secluded spot under them, and he, somewhat recovering, grasped me by the hand and drew me over there. I said nothing, as I was perfectly willing to let him do as he liked, and was sorry that he had stopped. We walked to the spot, and I noticed that there must have been others there before us, as the ground was covered with newspapers.

He pulled me down on the ground in a sitting posture and, sitting beside me, he again gathered me into his arms, kissed me and squeezed my breasts. I put my arms around his neck and kissed him back, and he then put his hand up under my dresses, which was easy as I had my legs wide open. He tried to slip his hand under the elastic bands of my bloomers on my leg, but gave up in disgust when he saw it was impossible.

I arose to my feet and, lifting my dresses, pushed the bloomers down and stepped out of them. I then laid them beside me and sat down again, and he placed his arms around me and kissed me.

I kissed him back, and his hand, again on my thighs, went at once to my cunt, and he pushed one of his fingers inside me. For a few minutes we lay there, me in his arms while he rubbed my cunt, and I kissing him madly. He took one of my hands in his and placed it on the front of his pants, and I felt that hard dagger leaping inside.

It seemed much bigger than I had expected it to be, and I began to be a little afraid of what I had started, but he opened his pants with his free hand and let it jump out before I had time to draw my hand away.

It was really nice-looking, about four inches long and possibly two or three inches around. At first there was some skin that covered it all, hanging over the head, but when he saw that I was so interested in this strange thing, he proudly drew back this covering skin and exposed to my gaze a red, swollen head.

'Is that the first prick that you have ever seen?' he asked me, shaking it at me.

I assured him that it was, and he took my hand, twined it around it and I squeezed it. It seemed to get harder while I held it in my hand. I examined it.

'Do you know why I brought you here, Edna?' he asked me, thrusting his finger in and out of me until I thought I would die with the pleasure he had started in me.

I told him that I supposed he wanted to fuck me, and I told him it was all right for him to go ahead so far as he liked.

'It's a go, then,' he said, and he kissed me again and, holding me around the waist, turned me on to my back on the grass and raised my dress up above my waist. I did not want him to see me naked like that – it seemed different than letting him feel me with his hand under my clothes – but I didn't want him to stop again, so I said nothing. I know my face must have been fiery red from shame.

Then his finger again moved into me and he moved it about rapidly until a terrible shudder ran over me, and I thought I was dead. In an instant my cunt was all wet.

'Now just a few minutes,' he said, 'and it will all be over. Let me lay between your thighs so that I can get at you, Edna.' At the same time he pulled my legs wide apart without me saying a single word.

Then he spit on the head of his prick, and drawing the skin well back, placed the bare head of it at the entrance of my cunt. He let it gently rest there.

'Take it in your hand,' he said, 'and guide it to just where my finger has been. Make yourself as limp as possible so it will feel simply grand.'

He was laying right on top of me, and at the same time he pressed his legs on my thighs, and pushed with his prick. It banged against my belly, and I took hold of it in my hand and steered it straight at my hole as he had told me to do.

A wonderful feeling came over me. I cannot describe it, only that it felt like I was fainting, with wonderful music playing in the background. Just as I was beginning to enjoy it the most, he pulled out of me, jumped up, and some kind of white stuff squirted out of the head of his prick in a shower on to the grass.

I was almost in tears with disappointment and asked him why he stopped. He told me that if he had let that load shoot off inside of me it might get me pregnant. I told him that it was just beginning to feel good when he jerked it out and he laughed and said, 'I suppose you would like to have me put it back into your belly, eh?'

'Yes, yes,' I said, opening wide my thighs, not caring now if he saw me or not.

'Look,' he said, and I looked at his prick. It had shrivelled away so that it was almost hidden in the hair of his belly. 'The next time,' he said, 'I will have a rubber, and then I can leave it inside of you. The rubber will keep the stuff from harming you. Now if you do not tell anyone, when we come down here again I will leave it pump in you, as it was only for your own good and protection that I pulled out of you.'

He made me promise not to tell anyone what we had done, and seemed scared that I would. You may imagine, girls, that this was too good to talk about and that I would say nothing to anyone that might cause trouble. Then he kissed me and gave me a few hugs, and I, seeing that he was not going to do it again, put on my bloomers. We started back home.

Then, the day before yesterday, he told me that if I wanted it again, he had a rubber with him and would leave his prick in me. Of course I was perfectly willing, and we went to the same place. After we had sat down and he put his hand under my clothes, he was surprised to find that I did not have any bloomers on.

I told him that I would never wear bloomers again, as I liked to be petted once in a while, and he said that was right. He soon had his prick out and I grabbed it, as I was not afraid of it. I pushed back the skin and rubbed it up and down in the manner he seemed to like. He stuck his finger in my cunt and I was soon hot, and he pushed me on my back and, with my hand guiding his prick, he soon had it stuck in me again.

This time it felt perfectly wonderful, and I moved about under it. He pushed it in and out, and I tell you, girls, there is nothing like a boy's prick to send thrills of delight through your soul!

For a while he kissed me and pushed it in and out of me while I lay there and enjoyed it. Then he pulled it out, put the rubber over it and put it back in.

I was surprised to find how easy it went in me, but I knew that I was all wet inside and that may have helped it. With the rubber on it, it felt bigger, but not as warm and nice. He was soon wiggling back and forth, so fast that I couldn't do anything but hold on to him with my legs and arms. Then, all of a sudden, he went limp and lay on me.

'There, Edna, you got all of it that time. How did you like it?' he panted.

'Oh,' I told him, 'please do it again. Do it all over again.' But all my begging and praying couldn't get him to get it hard again, and so that was all that I got.

While Edna had been telling her story, we had been fingering each other as fast as we could, and we were all just burning up. Then Mary jumped up and said, 'I have an idea, girls. Why not get something shaped just like a boy's prick and use that on ourselves in place of our fingers?'

For a while we could not think of anything, but finally Edna suggested that bananas would be just the thing. The cook was away, so we all ran downstairs, naked as we were, and as luck would have it, we found a big bunch of bananas in the icebox.

After some talking we decided that it would be best to leave the skins on, as we were not sure if they would be hard enough to stand up if we skinned them.

We took a knife and trimmed the end where the stalk was, and then each of us put one in our cunts as far as we could. It felt funny at first, then rather good, but holding them there and working them in and out got rather tiresome.

Then Edna suggested that Mary lie down on the bed, let her get on top of her and hold her legs tight together with the banana between her naked thighs. This would make her take the part of the man, and this way she would give Mary the pleasure of a fuck.

It worked fairly well until the skin of the banana broke and the banana oozed out, but when my turn came I got a real kick out of it. That was my first experience at being fucked, and that, of course, was by a girl. However, I made up my mind that I was going to have the real thing the first chance I could.

Time went on, and Mary and I were still permitted to spend our time together, as much as we wished. We had tried every way to get hold of a boy to fuck us, but so far had met with nothing but dismal failure. We had also tried all sorts of objects to fuck each other with, but we finally decided that bananas had the best shape. One day we had a wonderful idea. We went down to one of the department stores and bought some of the artificial fruit that they have on sale there, making sure that there were two bananas amongst the assortment.

As you know, this artificial fruit that is sometimes left on a table as a decoration is made out of some kind of wax, and these worked fine. We worried no more over disposing of the mashed fruit that used to result after a hard frigging on our part.

The day finally arrived when I was to start college, and with a good many heartaches I bid my friend Mary a tearful goodbye, and my father took me off to the school. I was assigned to a room with a very pretty young girl, about a year younger than myself. At that time I was about twenty years of age. For several weeks I was pretty busy getting started on my lessons and all the other things connected with schoolwork.

However, it was not long before I began wishing to feel the touch of something, anything, between my thighs. After going to bed I tried to satisfy myself with my finger, and took great care that my roommate would not detect me in the pleasure toss.

One night when I had been itching all day, I went to bed early, as I had obtained a banana, and hoped to use it before Betty, my roommate, would come in. Just about the time that I had reached the hottest point in my pokings, the door opened and in she came.

I do not know if she knew what I was doing, but she came over to the bed where I was lying and kissed me with her lips which, as you may imagine, almost set me off, and drawing away, she commenced to undress.

In a moment she was standing before the mirror, looking at herself and admiring her beautiful form. I did not at all blame her for this, for she had something to admire, and it set me hot to look at her. As if she was aware of my thoughts, she turned to me, and in doing so exposed to me all her lovely front. She was lovely and white, so tender and sweet were her cute, little belly and plump, well-mounded tits. Her hairy cave looked delectable. She walked about swinging her hips as though she was trying to entice me through sheer passion to grab her, pull her to me and make love to her.

Then she again came close to the bed and, bending over me, kissed me in that electric manner she had. Well, to make a long story short, when she did that I could not help myself. I was ready to die for it on the spot. I placed my hand on her soft fur.

Like a shot she sprang into the bed beside me. Her hand, as quick as lightning, shot down to my grotto. Finding the spot, her hand came in sudden contact with the banana that was impaled within me, and she almost screamed in amazement and fear.

'Mike, what is it? Are you a man? Tell me quick. If you are a man, or are gifted with a prick like one, fuck me and fuck me quick, as I have been dying for one and have been afraid to say anything,' she said.

Throwing off the covers, I let her see that I was just a girl like her own sweet self, but that the object that she had taken for a prick was capable of satisfying her.

'Oh, Mike,' she said, evidently disappointed that I was not a man, or that there was not a prick for her. 'I have something far better than that. Wait until I get it,' and jumping out of bed, she unlocked her trunk and soon found a metal box which she brought back to the bed.

'Look, Mike,' she said, 'my boyfriend presented me with this, and told me that if I ever felt like I wanted another boy, to resist the impulse if possible; but if it got too strong that it was impossible to bear it, I was to take this and put it inside of me and work it in and out of me until I felt relieved.

'I used it several times before I left home, but have been afraid to try it here, as you were in the room and I did not know if you would approve.'

As she was talking, she opened the box with a key and took out a hard rubber thing that looked a good bit like the banana I had, only it was larger and rounder.

'This is a perfect rubber prick, just like a man's,' Betty said, 'and I think that the both of us, judging from your actions, dear, can make good use of it!' She strapped it on her loins, pulled the banana out of my cunt, climbed over me, jammed that thing up in me and, with her bounces and heavings, soon had me in a seventh heaven of wonderful delight.

Of course I had to do for her what she had done for me, and you may believe me that we used that wonderful imitation of the thing we dreamed of. To some people this may seem very crude, especially for two young ladies, but you must consider that it was the only way that we knew of to satisfy the desires that burnt within us. We both longed for boys and the feel of a real prick, but we had no way of getting any, so we had to do the best that we could with what we had at hand.

I was delighted to find that Betty was of the same disposition as myself, and more so to find an object that would not mush or melt in my cunt. Many a royal battle we had with her cunt-provoker, as she laughingly called it.

One night one of the girls in the school came into our room with us for a while. She was older than either of us, and was a fine-looking girl. Her name was Gladys. She had a picture of a man and a woman loving each other, and she showed it to Betty and I, asking us if we didn't wish that we had a prick in us like that in the pictures.

We both agreed that we wished that we had. Then Betty goosed her, and I put my hand under her dress and found her cunt. It was moist and the lips were tingling.

'Oh, oh,' she said, pulling away from both of us and laughing, 'I see that you girls are not at all backwards in receiving company. You certainly know how to use your hands. But understand we are talking about pricks, and not jerking each other off.'

'If you really want it, Gladys,' said Betty, 'we can give you a bigger prick than that one in the pictures. Can't we, Mike?'

'Oh, yes,' I said, 'it is only rubber, but I'll wage you, Gladys, that it will make you dance. It sure does work.'

'Oh, let me see it, let me see it,' she said. 'I have never seen one. I have heard of them, but I have never seen one with my own eyes.'

Betty got it out and Gladys examined it, and even went to the extent of throwing up her dress and showing to us her pretty naked thighs as she pushed the tip of it in her cunt. 'It feels like the real thing,' she said. 'Where on earth did you get it?'

Betty told her, and we then made plans to have this pretty girl come to our room after the nine o'clock checkup.

'Of course,' Gladys agreed, and as soon as the teacher had passed our room at nine, we undressed and got into bed together. Gladys was not long in showing up, and she had already undressed and was in her pyjamas, quite ready for us.

In a second we had them off, and she was in the bed between us. Betty had strapped the prick, or, as it was called, dildo, on to her loins, and we soon had Gladys's thighs spread wide apart and Betty was on top of her belly sticking the prick into her cunt.

Soon she was writhing with pleasure.

~ 9 ~

La Tarantula

1934

The opera *Carmen* (1875) by the Frenchman Georges Bizet (1838–75) is one the finest and most recognised musical pieces in history. Based on an 1847 novel by Prosper Mérimée (1803–70), its tragic tale tells of the coquettish, tempestuous gypsy girl, who seduces a handsome military officer she fancies, and convinces him to release her and desert his post to join her in a life with the gypsies after she is arrested for stabbing a fellow cigarette factory worker. Tragedy ensues when his love becomes obsessive while hers cools in favour of a famous matador, and he stabs her to prevent her loss to another.

The theme of man, or woman, destroyed by uncontrollable and unrequited love is as old as history itself, and has been used too many times to list. Each 'new' literary genre feels constrained to incorporate it into its own *oeuvre*. In relatively modern times, the 1960s movie *Carmen Jones* is one such example. The 1935 Marlene Dietrich film *The Devil was a Woman* (based on the 1898 Pierre Louÿs tale 'Woman and her Puppet') was another such telling of a person destroyed by devotion to a scheming and worthless love object. *Carmen* is an intrinsically erotic story, though not sexually explicit, so one would expect the *sub rosa* 'hard core' sex genre to present its own representation of this classic tale. While this has not yet happened in a strict sense, one erotic novel of the 1930s does come close.

La Tarantula: An Erotic Tale of Spain by Don Luis de V— appeared in print in New York (not Seville as indicated on its title page) about 1934. Atypical for that day, it was finely printed on expensive paper from expertly set and artistically designed type. Its 6" x 9" format, printed soft cover, and six full-page illustrations were equally unusual for the underground literature of the time, putting it into the same league as the similarly produced and equally famous *Grushenka* and *The Prodigal*

Virgin (both reputedly published by a travelling bookseller named Percy Shustac). This was obviously an expensive production, limited to five hundred copies 'Privately Printed for the Accredited Subscribers of the Sociedad Erotico of Madrid'. Longtime bookmen remember this volume renting for $50 a week at the height of the Depression.

The central character of the novel, La Tarantula, is a sensuous Spanish gypsy girl, born in the same Triana section of Seville that *Carmen* made infamous. The novel opens with a quote from the *Encyclopaedia Britannica*, 'The [tarantula] is a poisonous spider. It spins no web as a snare but catches its prey because it is fleet of foot. Its home in the ground is lined with silk . . . ' Our namesake heroine was the most talented of entertainers. Her fleetness was in the agility of her dancing; her silks were the laces and shawls that decorated her home and boudoir. Her 'poison' metaphorically was that all her lovers, male and female, died unnatural and premature deaths! Perhaps it was magic; her birth had been heralded by a fire in a local porcelain factory, a possible omen that the pleasures she would afford would be accompanied by pain and death. She had many lovers. Her physical beauty, her seductive manner, her tempestuous nature, her grace and skill and fame as a dancer and singer, all attracted men and women to her like moths to a candle flame, and with equal results. She herself was of an overly hot-blooded nature, almost nymphomaniacal. Some lovers died from physical exertion, some from the consequences of their jealous actions, and some just died, victims of the curse that plagued her from birth.

This is obviously an erotic novel unlike any other in the English language. Elements of de Musset's *Gamiani* (1833) can be found in several of its episodes, as well as its overall misogynistic and morose tone. The same sullen atmosphere can be found in Alex Trocchi's *Thongs* (1956). While the sex scenes are highly graphic and detailed, there is no true *joie de vie*. The reader for one knows that tragedy is not far off, even if the characters do not. The prose is quite formal, and clipped, almost British one could say. The syntax is pedantic, so even the most unbridled and orgiastic scenes remain restrained, bound not by the words and actions, but by invisible, psychological boundaries imposed by the author's style. Humour when present is droll, the narrative style incessant and matter of fact. Like the opera *Carmen*, this literary work does not evade the sense of desperation and futility that controls its characters. The actors are powerless in the face of Fate. They are puppets in the hands of an unseen grand director, their actions, unknown to them, purely mechanical, no matter how mightily they strive for individual self-determination. Not even through sex acts, the venue of liberation for George Orwell's *Nineteen Eighty-Four* victims of totalitarianism, can they alter the inevitable.

As all sophisticated adults know, sex is not merely fun and games. Tabloid newspaper headlines sensationally remind us of this daily. There are psychological and emotional and physical complications of sexual liaisons, long or short term, which cannot be ignored. Erotic literature is usually escapist in nature (when not trying to be instructional). The following excerpt from *La Tarantula* demonstrates that erotica can on occasion be much more as well.

from *La Tarantula*

From that day on, the notoriety of La Tarantula was spread over the breadth of Spain. All knew of her talents as a gypsy dancer. Wherever a dancer was required it was she who was called in to supply that part of the entertainment. At the fairs, at benefits, at special performances where the services of gypsy Nina de los Peines, the Girl with the High Combs, who was the best singer in all Spain, were required, La Tarantula was called in.

And as her fame grew, La Tarantula became all the more reserved, in so far as men were concerned. Somehow or other, she seemed to sense that the gypsy in her, the wild carefree blood in her, made her the superior of the *bu'ne*, the ordinary gentiles of Spain. And the more she spurned them, the greater grew their desire for her. When she would dance for them, their eyes would follow her every movement, her every nuance of rhythm, and if she smiled at them, they would boast of the fact to their cronies for weeks afterwards.

But she soon discovered that, though the blood in her was gypsy blood, nevertheless it was human blood. The memory of that wild, tumultuous night with the guitarist Don Juan remained with her for some time. But she turned all thoughts of fucking away and concentrated on her dancing. From *cafetín* to *cafetín* she danced her way up the pathway of success. And in each place, she attracted another string of admirers who sought her favours. Like the swath of a comet they lay behind her as she shot her way upwards to the zenith. But to none of them did she give her cool body. It seemed as though the glorious fuckfest she had experienced that last night with Don Juan had served to tide her over a drought of men.

But this could not go on for any length of time. Hers was hot, southern blood, Spanish blood, Spanish gypsy blood that burned in her veins. That was why, one night, after she had spent a severe evening at the Café de las Flores in Seville on Calle de la Serpiente, the Street of the Serpents, she did as she did.

Lying back on her *chaise longue*, her limbs shaking from fatigue, she ruminated on the life she was leading. She looked out of the window that looked down on to the street. Streams of men were winding their way through the street. Men, men, men of all statures and forms and shapes. Men, men, all different yet all the same because all had that with which she had enjoyed herself so immensely and often.

Suddenly, she called out to her personal maid, 'Cazuela! Cazuela!'

That person came jogging in. She was an evil-looking thing. Only one eye gleamed out of her face. The other was only a dead black socket. You could not tell from looking at her that, at one time, like her mistress, she had been the leading Spanish gypsy in Spain, that her roughened, toadlike skin had once been as velvet-smooth as La Tarantula's, that her shapeless limbs and arms had once been as straight and fine as her attractive mistress's.

Years ago, when she had danced, a lover had beaten her up and, in doing so, had kicked her eye out with the heel of his boot. She became unwanted from that day on, as a dancer. But she never slept with another man. Them she hated worse than she hated anything else in the world. She became as complete a man-hater as there was, carrying her hatred to the point of lesbianism. She had learned early in life the pleasures of woman love and had practised it incessantly. La Tarantula had picked her up one night, during the early part of her career, and from her had learned of the subtle arts of the dancer. For Cazuela had taught her everything that she herself had known about the art of dancing. Everything she taught her except one thing. About the love of woman for woman, she said nothing. She only bided her time until she could feel that her mistress would be most receptive to its practice. Meanwhile she acted as the personal maid of La Tarantula and taught her all the intricacies of the *baile* flamenco and the Sevilliana and the *baile* Malaga, the soleadina and the fandango and the paso doble, until La Tarantula became even more adept at them than had been her teacher. Then it was that she had started on the meteoric rise which landed her finally as the star attraction at Café de las Flores, the most beautiful café on the Street of Serpents in Seville, co-starring with the greatest romantic tenor of Spain, none other than Señor Don Jose Calorá himself, from Lima, Peru.

And that was where we found her at the start of this chapter, in her dressing room upstairs from the café resting from her labours after an extremely difficult hour of dancing the paso doble for the customers who had clapped again and again for encores. Next door, in the other dressing room, she heard Señor Don Jose going though his vocal exercises. Then all was quiet. Then it was that she summoned her maid Cazuela.

'Yes, mistress?' she enquired on entering. She saw that the dancer was lying outstretched in the attitude of complete exhaustion.

'I am tired! So tired!' La Tarantula complained.

'Does my mistress desire a massage?' the woman asked, continuing further with, 'such as I was taught many years ago by my old dancing teacher Don Ortega?'

'Anything! Anything!' La Tarantula cried. 'Anything to take away the terror of the pain in my poor, tired muscles! Oh! why must I dance? Why must I continuously dance for men, filthy men!' And saying this, she turned her face to the pillow and buried it in her arms and wept.

She lay in this fashion for a few minutes, taking pleasure in knowing that she was suffering, as women are apt to do. Then she felt a pair of cool hands settle on her thighs. And the hands began to knead the flesh and muscles to and fro, working the tiredness out of them, flexing the rawness out of them that made them feel as though they had been weighted with lead. All over her body she felt the expert fingers of Cazuela roam, until she felt the tiredness slip away, fall away like a heavy velvet cloak from her shoulders. It seemed as though she were floating on gossamer clouds now, as though her body had left her entirely, and that she was all mind. And that her mind was hovering up above her body like a disembodied spirit and pitying the hulk of a body that lay on the *chaise longue*. Lightness, softness, cushiony nothingness was all about her.

Suddenly she felt a slow, intense throb shoot into her.

She opened her eyes wide. There, between her legs, she saw Cazuela, her face pushed in between the joint of her legs as closely as she could get it. But, what was more, she was working her tongue into her mistress's cunt, like forked lightning, touching the button of the clitoris so that it jerked up in sudden surprise. The jerk of the clitoris caused La Tarantula to open her eyes. For the moment, she thought of ordering the woman away from her. Disgust was the first reaction to what she saw. But, pleasure was the immediate reaction to what she felt. Pleasure, the likes of which she had never before experienced. Pleasure, such as she had felt when she has been fucked by Don Juan, and that she had sedulously kept herself from these last long years. Pleasure, pleasure filling her with an inordinate amount of desire.

In and out she felt the smooth tongue of Cazuela dart, touching, it seemed, the very vital spot in her system, drawing the blood from her throbbing heart to her throbbing clitoris so that it stood up now like a living thing.

Before she could realise it, La Tarantula felt the ominous approach of the orgasm. Just as she had felt it coming on before, with the man, so she felt it rapidly drawing nearer, but with a woman.

'What should I do?' she wailed, 'I am coming!'

'Hold it as long as you can!' the maid managed to gasp out between licks as she sank her tongue deeper into La Tarantula's cunny. 'Help me by tickling my button!' and, in order to aid her, she drew herself up closer to her mistress and lifted her dress high above her hips. La Tarantula got the idea immediately, and, as she sucked in her guts and withheld the load that was piling up within her, she reached over and inserted her index finger into the throbbing but enlarged cunt of her maid. The first thought that came to her was a comparative one. She thought of how large Cazuela's cunt was as compared to her own diminutive one. But this thought remained for only a moment. She had no time to think. Feelings, emotions, crowded her consciousness until they threatened to overflow in one vast, heaving surge of passionate floodtide.

Thus the pair of them worked together, each trying to titillate the other into a blessed orgy of spending their essences for each other. Closer and closer La Tarantula felt her own orgasm approaching as her maid's tongue darted faster and faster in the overheated box that was her cunt. And under her own fingers she felt the little soldier of Cazuela's clitoris stiffen to attention. Soon she was panting as though she were winded, as she panted after an unusually exhausting fandango. And she began to throw her loins around as though the prick of a man were ramming itself into her. She heard the same laboured breathing of her maid. And she felt the severe thrusts of the woman's buttocks, jerking nervously in a Saint Vitus's dance of passion. Faster and faster each tickled the other. Closer and closer came their orgasms. Louder and louder grew the sound of their heavy panting.

Suddenly, La Tarantula heard her maid moan as though she had lost the most precious of things. And over her hand she felt the gushing warmth of a sticky liquid spurting out in hot viscid jets. The moment she felt the wetness she felt the maid's body exert itself mightily in one grand upheaval. La Tarantula could hold herself no longer She felt the overflowing in the region of her loins, in the small of her back. Her breath came faster. Her hips vibrated madly. Her tongue clove to the top of her parched mouth. Not knowing what she was doing, she seized hold of Cazuela's cunt and squeezed it so that the poor maid shrieked. With her other free hand, she dug her fingers into the *chaise longue* so that the long fingernails ripped jagged tears in the cloth.

Then she came!

Pouring, spurting out of her abnormally heated cunny came the pearly fluid full into the face of the maid who was still working on the poker-stiffened clitoris. For a while both of them continued to work their bodies jerkily as the intense feeling that swarmed over them remained. But when it started its decline, each fell away from the other, La Tarantula on her back against the *chaise longue*, Cazuela on the floor, each gasping from their exhaustion. Completely tired, they remained in these positions, their eyes closed, their arms outspread, a lush feeling of tired warmth creeping over their limbs.

They were suddenly startled by the sound of clapped palms. La Tarantula opened her eyes wildly to see that the clapping was coming from the doorway. And, in the doorway, she saw the immense portly figure of Don Jose Calorá, the South American tenor who was co-starring with her that week. She became speechless. Shame crept over her. Her cheeks reddened like an over-bloomed rose.

'Pretty! Pretty! Very pretty!' the tenor said, still clapping his palms together daintily, in derision.

'What do you want here?' La Tarantula demanded.

'I heard the sound of your ardent lovemaking in my rooms,' the tenor continued with a shrug. 'The walls are so thin. I thought it my duty to see what I could do in the way of helping you wonderful ladies!'

La Tarantula looked from the tenor to her maid who was reclining on the floor, hatred shooting from her eyes, hatred for the man who had interrupted her orgy of lesbianism.

'Don't be afraid, my dear!' the tenor continued, advancing slowly to the pair near the window. And as he advanced, he threw his wide-brimmed sombrero aside and started to take off the velvet pea jacket that he was wearing.

Still, neither La Tarantula nor her maid spoke. Instead they watched the man disrobe, as they were completely hypnotised by his actions. They saw him undo the sash around his great belly, and then slip off his shoes and draw his bellbottomed trousers off. La Tarantula gasped when she saw his enormous prick shoot out from its confining quarters. But the maid sneered and her lips curled in disdain.

When the tenor had disrobed himself completely, he towered over the two shrinking women like an enormous man mountain, his girth quivering like jelly, his cock sticking out from its bed of dark brown hair like a jousting pole in the arm of a medieval knight.

'Really, ladies!' he said, advancing still closer to them, 'you are wasting the charms of two beautiful woman when you attempt to draw pleasure from each other by yourselves. Woman was made for man's pleasure. And, likewise man was made for woman's pleasure. Neither can derive pleasure from themselves. You are women. I am a man. Quite a man,' he continued, stroking his swollen piece for emphasis.

But La Tarantula scarcely heard a word he was saying. Her eyes were for nothing but the projecting prick, as big as life, swollen beyond the size of any other penis.

'You like it, eh?' the tenor asked.

La Tarantula nodded her head. Cazuela began to lose some of her disrespect for the man. After all, this was no ordinary man, she reasoned. Any man with a cock like that stood apart from the world in general and man in particular. And she too could look at nothing but that great big *bravo toro*, that could have done service even for a stud bull.

With a huge, roaring laugh, he eased himself directly over the body of La Tarantula as she lay back on the *chaise longue*, wondering what was going to be the outcome of this strange affair with this strange man.

'Spread your legs!' the tenor said imperiously. But he could not see to insert his stiffened prick into her cunt, although she spread her legs as wide as she could. It was his hanging belly. Like all tenors, he ate well and had built up a large-size physique so that he would have great lungs for a powerful voice. And so his belly, hanging over his prick, prevented him from directing it into its proper channel.

Suddenly he turned to where Cazuela was lying on the floor staring wide-eyed at the proceedings. 'Help me in with the thing, woman!'

Slowly she arose to a kneeling position and took hold of the rampaging prick. Beneath its skin she felt a pregnancy of power that seemed to be striving mightily to burst the bonds that were holding it. Life coursed through its entire length with the vivacity of a dozen men. The steady throb of blood pumping through it made it seem like a living thing, an entity in itself, as though it were apart from the rest of the body. Tenderly she wrapped her ten fingers around its haft. All hatred for the male sex was driven out of her.

With her right hand she spread apart the lips of La Tarantula's vagina as wide as she could possibly move them. Then, directing the pulsating phenomenon, she guided it slowly, surely between the parted ruby lips of the quivering quim of La Tarantula, stroking its entire length as the whole of it slid into the awaiting aperture with a succulent sound of suction.

Immediately there arose from La Tarantula a moan such as of a woman going through the travail of childbirth. In her she felt the parting of her body. But it was such sweet pleasure. What was Chato Doble? What was Don Juan? This was a man! Her breath almost left her when she felt the size of the thing pushing its way insistently into her, spreading her apart, touching the very quick of her existence.

'Oh! Oh! Oh!' was all she could say as she worked her hips. The inner part of her cunt was well-lubricated with the juice of her spurting brought on by Cazuela's titillating of her clitoris. Oiled by the pearly fluids, the cock was sinking deeply into her like a machine piston moving up and back. Each time it moved forward it shoved in a little deeper. And each time it shoved in a little deeper, she cried out, not knowing that she was crying out, knowing only that in her was the greatest thing in the world.

Before she was aware of what was happening, she felt the curious boiling within her. She was coming. Before she had an opportunity to prepare for it, she spurted her fluid. It was the size of his thing that was the reason for it. And so she threw her arms around his enormous belly, clutched the flesh and panted like a wounded hart. And, without a warning, she felt herself let go of herself. But, at the same time, she felt a splashing of fluid within her such as she had never before experienced. There must have been a whole pint in his bulking balls for she felt it streaming in hot gushes all over her cunt and, in a short while, she felt the excess fluid trickling slowly down her leg.

Instead of withdrawing his penis, the tenor allowed it to remain where it had been. 'It takes so long for it to come back to its normal shape, you may as well get as much pleasure out of it as you can,' he explained to her. Completely spent, La Tarantula allowed her head to loll over to the side. She saw Cazuela frantically fingering her own clitoris, pitifully trying to bring herself to another climax. And just as La Tarantula turned her way, she managed to bring herself up to the desired climax. Her body went through a series of contortions. She locked her legs together as tightly as she could get them. Her face wrinkled itself in a spasm of passion. Then she came. And her whole body stiffened up into a huge knot.

There they lay, the three of them, La Tarantula exhausted from the severe fucking she had received, the tenor puffing from the mere physical exertion of wielding his prick, and the maid, Cazuela, outstretched on the floor, the fluid issuing from her stretched cunt. For a while, no one spoke a word. The only sound to be heard was the stentorous breathing of the three of them puffing like winded runners. La Tarantula's eyes were closed. As she felt the gradual decline of the cock within her, she felt a curious feeling of reluctance go through her, reluctance to let go of that marvellous instrument that had afforded her so much pleasure in such a little time. But she felt it grow smaller and smaller in her. In time it subsided completely. But she continued to rest back, her eyes closed, a delicious sense of well-being enveloping her as the after-fuck settled over her limbs and gave her a feeling of satisfaction.

At last La Tarantula cocked her ears for familiar sounds. In the distance, faintly, she could hear the concerted twang of the string orchestra in the café below. Outside, in the street, she heard the cry of an itinerant lottery-ticket seller calling, 'The winning number! Remember it! Buy now or weep tomorrow!' Gradually, his cry lessened until the street was quiet once again. The rhythmic breathing of her maid came up to her. She had probably fallen asleep after her double spurting of dew. But how about the tenor? Why was he not breathing as heavily as he had done before? Without opening her eyes, she strained her ears to catch a sound of his breathing. But no sound came. For a while, she made nothing of it. But a small doubt insisted on remaining in her mind. Again she tensed herself and listened for the sound of his breathing. But still no sound came. She was afraid to open her eyes. Instead, she lay back, her heart filled with a dread fear, her throat stopped up with an unreleased sob. Then, with all her might, she finally managed to force her eyelids apart. They widened with terror when she gazed at the face of the tenor hovering directly over her. Instead of the jovial countenance that had been there before, there was a horrid purple mask. Tiny red veins seemed to have appeared all over his bloated face. His eyes seemed to have popped out of their sockets. Tiny flakes of slobber drivelled out of the corners of his mouth. But worst of all were the great white eyeballs protruding from their holes like a frog's pop eyes.

La Tarantula shrieked in horror.

Then she realised that her suspicions had been correct. On top of her, astride of her in the attitude of fuck, was the hulking body of a dead man. Already she felt what had been warm flesh only a short while ago, rapidly turning cold. Like one gone suddenly berserk, mad, she tried to wriggle herself free from the dead weight of the three-hundred-pound corpse that was imprisoning her. But with her weakened strength further lessened by the two orgasms she had just undergone, she was unable to get herself away from under the gruesome cadaver. Her shrieks awakened Cazuela. She too shrieked when she saw the purplish, bloated face of the tenor. Then, when she came to her senses, when she finally realised the predicament her mistress was in, she leaped up, seized hold of La Tarantula's arms, and dragged her slowly from under the triangle of the man's spread knees. Immediately, when this was done, the body toppled over to one side, its horrible face upward, its body already stiffened in the throes of rigor mortis.

Later on, at the inquest, the coroner called it heart failure. They did not hold La Tarantula, despite the deaths that had occurred in her presence previously. There had been no doubt as to the cause of the death of the tenor. His heart, already overburdened by the enormous weight that he carried around with him, simply buckled under when he went through the terrific exertions of that last fuck with La Tarantula. The coroner called it heart failure. But the old men, sunning themselves in the square, they nodded their heads knowingly and cackled when the news of the inquest was brought around. They cackled because they knew that the tarantula had struck again. They knew that the death's head had shown its ugly face and had brought down another victim.

And when the news of the death of Cazuela was delivered, they nodded their heads again. The reports stated that she had mistaken a bottle of poison for a bottle of aguardiente. She had been found lying in the anteroom of La Tarantula's dressing room. Her face was screwed up into a mass of wrinkles. Bitterness, the bitterness of the wormwood and the gall of the poison was etched in those lines. Her stomach was distended from the virulence of the poison. A stale odour of almonds hung in the air. The coroner called it accidental poisoning. But the old greybeards whispered, 'The tarantula has struck again.'

M. Fontaine's Establishment

1935

They say New York City was once a quaint little town, whatever that meant. True there were bygone days when people still felt safe walking the streets or parks any time of the day or night. Yet New York City always had the justified reputation as a tough and criminal place. Whether it was the notorious eighteenth-century Paradise Alley in lower Manhattan , with its boast of at least one murderous attack every single night, or the infamous Five Points section near City Hall and the ubiquitous public and political corruption of Tammany Hall in the nineteenth century, or the Prohibition-gangland-drug-war-induced violence we are still plagued with daily, New York has had more than its share of crooks and crime.

Of all its vices, sex for sale is the one New Yorkers seem least likely to want suppressed. Prostitution, brothels and kept mistresses are an indispensable part of the colour and charm that has made the City. Who hasn't heard of Forty-Second Street as the sex capital of the United States? Today there are street walkers on the corners of the entire city, high-priced call girls (and boys) spread out from the Upper East Side, sado-masochistic parlours hidden in lofts throughout the five boroughs, and all openly advertised in sex papers, handbills, and cable TV. The 1920s had its famous 'Tenderloin' district in what is now Chelsea; New York brothels of the nineteenth century rivalled those of New Orleans and San Francisco, and were frequented by the highest of society. One of the earliest American erotic novels, *Cicily Martin*, describes an 1832 brothel on Leonard Street, below Canal Street and just off Broadway, frequented by the early Wall Street set. To this day, the 'best kept' mistresses are given apartments of their own, saving their lovers the expense and embarrassment of hotels. It is said that the Brooklyn and Manhattan Bridges were built so close together to accommodate the deluge of wealthy lower-Manhattan businessmen rushing to their Brooklyn-Heights-ensconced girlfriends for lunchtime 'quickies' or a fast tumble before returning to their homes at night. How many Fifth Avenue millionaires had around-the-corner Madison Avenue hideaways for their mistresses one will never know.

M. Fontaine's Establishment describes a fictitious house of pleasure located on a mythical street in Manhattan. *Cognoscenti* of the City will recognise the description of the area as fitting Greenwich Village in the 1920s and 1930s, especially the area around Bleecker, Hudson, Grove and Bedford Streets. (A 1980s *New York Magazine* article listed one of the City's best whorehouses as still being in the Village.)

This novel was first printed about 1935 and appeared in five small fascicles, which were latter sold as a single bound volume. Neither the title page nor contents gave any clue as to the real author. The writing style was light and breezy. The language carried the rough cadence of pure American lingo and read more like an extended magazine story than a novel. (The late Jack Hanley, 'Gene Harvey', was one writer of the era who frequently crossed between the *sub* and *supra rosa* worlds of periodical fiction.) *M. Fontaine's Establishment* well captured the flavour of the day, especially as to the peccadilloes of the idle, bored and generally jaded wealthy and powerful during the heart of the Depression. From the Irish cop on the beat to the deviant political nabob, here was New York illicitly at play. A liberal-minded foreigner provided the playground, and collected the fees for the meaningless assignations of his clients. The sexual liaisons were discreet, anonymous, and all sexual proclivities between consenting adults were catered to.

Of particular interest in this American novel, is the inclusion of both male and female homosexuality, in graphic and sympathetic detail. Before bisexuality became 'radically chic' in the 1980s, such a mix of sexual descriptions in a single novel was uncommon. Male gay activity was usually only hinted at in American published books of the 1930s, even in specifically gay-themed ones such as *The Scarlet Pansy* or *Escal Vigour*. Rare exceptions with sexually explicit male homosexual scenes included *Crimson Hairs* and the totally gay *Youthful Days*. The homosexual-directed slang used by the author may seem disparaging to the contemporary ear and sensibilities but in fact represents the genuine argot of the time, as equally recorded in the 'adult' humour collection *Anecdota Americana* (1927).

This novel in the legion of world literature would rank near the 'amateur' level. It is a simple declarative story, in simple words, with no message beyond 'uninhibited sex is fun' and 'live and let live'. There is little psychological eroticism. Physical coition and instant gratification of the lusts are its foremost themes. All the sex is 'happy sex', unencumbered and an end unto itself. Men and women are sexual equals in this tale of fornication. There is humour, albeit grotesque at times, and even the direst of consequences are turned into ironic successes. There are orgy scenes comparable to those in the Victorian masterpiece *The Romance of Lust*, and a cavalier attitude toward all expressions of sexuality unmatched since Lord Rochester's *Sodom* (1684).

Here then is an excerpt where Walsh, the local patrolman, finally investigates the suspicious shop of M. Fontaine, and is admitted through a secret entrance by the gay doorman, who calls himself Lucy.

⌒ from *M. Fontaine's Establishment*

Walsh awoke the following day at noon, very impatient to investigate further the strange comings and goings at the establishment of M. Fontaine. He was like a bloodhound on a scent. Suddenly he was struck with the idea of, as he expressed it, 'crashing the joint'. He acted immediately on the thought by putting on fine linen, donning a civilian business suit of aristocratic black, topping himself off with a black derby. He also added the touch of a silk handkerchief for the breast pocket and a cane for his wrist. He had found it one night on his beat and he carried it a trifle clumsily, for the technique was rather different from that of the club.

It was almost three o'clock when he idled along the opposite side of the street from Fontaine's. He was rewarded within a half-hour with the individual appearance of three men and four women, who entered the hallway and made for the rear. The patrolman's last doubt melted away.

'Here goes,' he said to himself. 'I'll probably make a hash of it, but I can't lose anything.'

A few minutes after he pushed the button, the lock clicked and he went into the anteroom. He opened the drawers of the cabinet and noticed that there were more masks than he had seen the previous evening.

'That settles that,' he grunted grimly. 'They all wear masks when they go in, so this little boy does the same.'

He put on a mask and adjusted it tightly. Then, being a man of little hesitation, he pressed the button and heard the buzzer sound above the vague murmur of voices behind the door. He did not have long to wait. Lucy appeared, fresh as a daisy.

'You wish a lady or a gentleman?' came the astounding question with ingratiating inflection.

Oho, thought Walsh. It's all coming out now. 'A lady,' he answered tensely.

'In the usual way – or otherwise?'

'The usual way.'

'Very well, sir. You will pay the usual fee.'

Walsh thought fast and took a chance. 'Ten dollars, isn't it?'

'Oh, no! You must have forgotten. Twenty dollars.'

'Oh you,' mumbled the policeman, and he reached for his wallet. He extracted two ten-dollar notes, which almost exhausted his cash, and tendered them to Lucy. The latter opened the door with a key, for it had locked automatically behind her, and inclined her head for Walsh to follow. They entered the room of mystery. The policeman was a bit bewildered by the soft lights and the penetrating perfume. Lucy led him to a vacant room and promised to return soon with a lady.

His eyes became engrossed with the pictures on the walls. He had often seen such pictures, but none as good as these. The policeman's peter soon began to rise and his tongue became thick in his mouth. When he had exhausted the pictures he listened with amusement to the sounds made by the revellers in the other rooms. Then he started all over on the pictures, noticing little things he hadn't seen before. The delightfulness of firm, round flesh inflamed his desires so that he was unconscious of the passage of time. He was brought to his senses by the entrance of a masked woman, beautifully dressed and exquisitely formed. She set the automatic lock as she closed the door and turned to Walsh with a dazzling smile, her perfect teeth glistening in a carmine setting and her eyes sparkling through her mask.

'How do you do?' she greeted him with composure.

Walsh's heart began to pound and he found speech difficult. Licking his lips, he managed to get out a whisper: 'All right. And how are you?'

She came to him, still smiling, and held out her arms for an embrace. Walsh reached mechanically. He crushed her to him, but with a throaty laugh she bent backward, drawing him with her.

'You're beautiful,' he murmured.

'How original you are,' she laughed. Will you help me out of my clothes?'

The officer assisted her with trembling fingers, feeling all parts of her warm and pulsating body – her breasts, her waist and buttocks, her perfectly rhymed thighs, and he finally got his hand on the cherished slit between her legs. He smoothed aside the downy herbage around her vulva and inserted his finger. Withdrawing it a little moist, he brought it to his eager nostrils and sniffed, while she laughed intoxicatingly at his antics. She was now naked and wanted to help him off with his clothes with lightning speed. Then they sat down on the couch and he played with her cunt while she toyed with his penis.

'Stalwart as a soldier, ready for battle, isn't he?' she murmured languidly. 'How ambitious he is. I'm beginning to feel good now, so let's do it. Are you ready?'

She stretched out on the couch, lifting her lovely legs up and apart as Walsh spread a towel and a pillow under her plump buttocks. Then he mounted to perform his duty. With her help he eased his rigid member into her vagina, which was warm and moist, and she twined her limbs tightly about his. Resting firmly on his knees, he placed one hand under her, while with the other he explored all of her jewels that he was able to. She, on her part, reached her arms around him and gripped the cheeks of his arse with both hands. And gently they moved their buttocks together and apart, drawing away from each other only for the purpose of coming together again. They were well-matched, for the fit was not too tight and yet not too loose, and at every stroke he plunged his sword as far as it would go into its scabbard. His bollocks began to drum a tattoo against her buttocks. She sighed, entranced, and murmured endearments to him.

'You're wonderful, wonderful.'

'And you're all right, too,' he replied, being now perfectly at home, and feeling altogether the dominant male.

Faster, faster, they went. The ancient and hallowed rhythm of love. More and more excited they became. Now they were both perspiring and breathing hard, their flesh was on fire; all the world was forgotten; only the moment of passion mattered. But all things come to an end. Walsh was the first to come. He announced it to her beforehand, regretfully.

'I'll be with you in a minute,' she told him in a trembling breath. 'Ah! Ah! Faster! Faster! Hold me tighter. I'm coming! Ah!'

She melted away before his prick grew soft and they rested in each other's arms, at peace with all things and completely contented. They had fulfilled themselves, had justified their existence with the universe. A minute thus, and at her unexpressed desire, which he divined instinctively, they separated and washed their parts, chatting gaily the while.

'I feel like a stimulant,' she said. 'Shall we ring for some cognac and cigarettes?'

'Sure, of course.'

She rang and Lucy came promptly. Walsh opened the door a bit and communicated their needs to her. And in doing so he made an error. He forgot to disguise his voice and the attendant immediately recognised him, for she was extremely sensitive to sounds. However, she brought the cognac and cigarettes on a tray which she handed in through the partly opened door.

'I'll pay you afterwards,' said Walsh.

Lucy was in a panic. She speedily acquainted her employer, who was in the shop, with the condition of affairs.

'We'll all go to jail now,' she lamented with a sob in her throat.

'You must keep calm,' advised M. Fontaine gently. 'Everything will be all right, I assure you. I have foreseen this for some time. I knew something like it would happen sooner or later. Of course I shall have to pay blackmail to him. But I wonder how much. Or rather how little.'

'Oh, what shall I do?' asked Lucy mournfully.

'You must attend to your duties and let me do the worrying,' said M. Fontaine. 'You must not forget that most of our patrons are rich and influential. Such people do not go to jail. Everything will be all right, so go back now.'

Lucy returned to her *ménage* but could not regain her customary confidence.

Meanwhile, the masked lady was sitting in Walsh's lap, his cock between her legs. They began to play with each other. He rubbed her slit while she prankishly tipped his rosy cock gently so that it swung from side to side. They kissed and bit each other lightly, thus developing their reviving passion. He also took a great delight in sucking the nipples of her breasts, firm and curved like young cantaloupes. What voluptuous pleasures were theirs – the proximity of flesh to flesh, the mingling of two desires into one and the anticipation of the coming action. Soon they were ready, for they were both young. Ah, youth – youth is always ready! And so again they travelled the road to Paradise, riding the fiery steeds of love. And again they mounted higher and higher up the steps of heaven until they reached the throne, the brilliant blazing goal of all lovers – past, present, and those as yet unborn. After their climax they rested quite a while, his prick still in her vagina, both veiled in a haze of languor. Presently they arose, and with a great calm upon them, they washed and dressed. Walsh attired himself very quickly and, kissing her mischievously on the arse, made ready to leave.

'*Au revoir* then,' she said. 'Perhaps we shall meet here again. I hope so, because you carry such a fine standard with you. I generally come in the afternoon, about two or three times a week. You will not forget?'

'No, I won't forget,' he promised her, 'but let me see your face, won't you?' He made a move to take off her mask.

'Don't do that,' she cried angrily, seizing his extended hands.

'Oh, all right!' he said soothingly, 'I was only fooling. Goodbye!'

'Goodbye!'

Feeling a little foolish, Walsh let himself out and found himself in the corridor, confronted by Lucy, who was somewhat agitated.

'Well, if it isn't little Percival!' the officer remarked banteringly.

'I am known as "Lucy",' was the retort.

'Lucy! Well, well, and how's Lucy today?' raising his voice to a high pitch.

'Very well, sir,' sulkily. 'And if you are leaving now I hope you will not forget that you owe me for the liquor and for the cigarettes.'

'Forget about it,' declared Walsh in his ordinary workaday voice. 'You're lucky I don't pinch you. Right now I want to see your boss. Lead me to him.'

'Very well,' assented Lucy sullenly. 'But you must take off the mask.'

The officer did so and he was taken into the shop and into the presence of M. Fontaine. That gentleman gestured to Lucy to return to her charges, and, as the latter disappeared, he turned to Walsh with an affable smile.

'I hope you've enjoyed yourself this afternoon, officer,' he ventured.

Walsh, for some reason, had lost a considerable modicum of his confidence. His words and his manner indicated nervousness. He licked his lips repeatedly. M. Fontaine noticed this at once and twisted his moustache with satisfaction, though he was at a loss to account for it.

'Y'know, Mr Fontaine – I, oh, I ain't got any bad feeling against you for running a place like that,' he jerked his thumb toward the rear room. 'That's your business, and of course anybody who fools with these rich people is going to get into hot water himself. But – '

'Ah!' thought the antique dealer. 'I shall not have to pay him very much. That is plain.'

Then aloud: 'You paid the attendant twenty dollars, did you not officer?'

'Yeh, I did.'

'I presume you would like it back?'

'Yeh. Sure I would.'

M. Fontaine drew a roll from his pocket, peeled off a twenty and gave it to Walsh, at which it vanished speedily.

'Thanks, Mr Fontaine. You know I'll keep mum about your place, but, I, ah, well – '

'You?' smilingly.

'Well, it's this way!' the policeman blurted out. Then his voice dropped to a whisper as he moved very close to the proprietor. 'Y'see, I like to suck women's cunts now and then, but I don't often get much chance. I've been wondering if you'd let me come sometimes for nothing. I can't afford to throw out twenty bucks. And I'll keep shut up like a clam.'

An illuminated smile broke out on the face of M. Fontaine.

'Oho! So that's it, my friend! But you needn't have been ashamed of it. I sympathise most heartily with you. You know, my friend,' confidentially, 'that I, too, often drink from the fountain of joy. Ah most certainly, officer! Come whenever you like and just tell Lucy what you want.'

Walsh wiped the perspiration from his forehead, looked at his watch, and decided that he must go. He was escorted to the front door and bade the antique dealer *adieu*.

'We are good friends, then, are we not?' asked M. Fontaine suavely.

'Yeh, sure.'

'And you may come whenever you like and it will cost you not a penny.'

'Thanks! Say! – how about right now?'

'Surely, it you wish it.'

They went back to the rear room and consulted the attendant.

'Try room seven,' suggested that functionary, 'but I'm not certain.'

In number seven Walsh found a very aristocratic-appearing lady of middle age.

'Hello,' he began nervously.

'Good evening! I've been waiting quite a while for someone.'

She scrutinised him carefully through her mask and smiled.

Walsh wetted his lips with his tongue in anticipation.

'The attendant, ah, told me you like to do it, ah, different ways.'

'Which way do you wish to do it?'

'I like to suck it,' he answered, his face turning redder than it usually was.

'I'm agreeable,' she said, 'but not completely.'

'What do you mean?'

'Well, you can suck it halfway,' she explained in a strained tone, 'And then finish up in the ordinary fashion. I'd like that better.'

'All right! – I'm willing.'

They undressed hastily, Walsh all the time feeling ill at ease. His heart played him queer tricks, the blood rushed in his ears and his whole body was possessed by the trembles.

She stretched out on the couch and spread her legs, lifting the knees. Her skin was like alabaster and unblemished, yet Walsh wished that she were plumper and younger. But that left his mind as he gazed centredly at her foliage-protected nest. He got up on the couch, his cock hard and throbbing, and, resting on his knees, made ready to drive into the source of all masculine joy.

'Not yet,' she protested, 'you poor boy. How like an amateur you go at it. Aren't you ashamed of yourself? Come here to me.'

He bent down and took the nipple of one of her breasts in his mouth and began to suck it. At once she took his prick in her hand and stroked it downward until she reached the sperm-tank underneath. She played with that and talked gently to him.

'You ought to know,' she instructed him, 'that a woman always likes to be played with before she gets into action.'

He let go of her nipples.

'I think you're a very nice girl,' he advanced. 'I wonder if you'll let me kiss you?'

'Try it and see,' was her answer.

His lips sought hers and, as her arms linked around his neck, they met in a long, warm kiss. She sighed as their lips parted and they kissed again and again.

'You know how to kiss,' she admitted as his lips travelled downward. He fiercely lipped her throat and breasts and slightly curved abdomen, below the entrancing dimple of her navel.

'I'm ready for your attention lower down,' she said, 'but remember, when I tell you to stop, I want you to finish up with your rod. Such a handsome one you have, too.'

'I'll remember, honey,' he assured her. 'And when I get through you won't be sorry you took me on.' He assumed again the position he had had at first, and in a moment his mouth was tightly pressed against her vulva, and he worked his tongue in and out, exciting her clitoris at every stroke. She clipped her thighs around his head and the feel of the warm flesh spurred his desire and made his fiery member strike against his belly. The taste of her cunt set him in a fever and his nostrils drank in greedily the odour of her organs mingled with the heady perfume she used. Her loving words goaded him into a frenzy. Sucking and mouthing madly he had only enough control left to keep from biting, a procedure he really would have liked to follow.

Suddenly she cried passionately: 'Enough! Enough! Now mount me.' He was not slow in obeying.

'Oh! You dear!' she breathed as his cock drove into her burning cunt. 'Oh! You sweet one! How good you are. I'll take it all back; there's nothing amateurish about you. Push harder! Faster! Deeper! As deep as you can. Oh, you wonderful man.'

Her legs were closed tightly around his hams and she clasped him so wildly around the back that it seemed as though she were afraid he would try to break away. And he rode his maddened charger in and out as hard as he could, while her buttocks heaved and tossed and rolled like waves in a tempest.

Soon she had her orgasm and lost all control of herself and bounced up and down, while she sighed and groaned, her breath coming in rasps. In a few minutes she was quiet, but he, like a raging bull, rammed his tool in and out of her flooded vagina. Suddenly he stopped, for her buttocks were quiet.

'I haven't come yet,' he panted. 'Aren't you going to help me out?'

'Yes, my dear,' she sighed languidly, 'but you must be gentle with me now.'

Very slowly they began moving together and apart in perfect harmony. Walsh received keen enjoyment from this method, but he felt as though he would never come. His desire was to drive furiously, but he wanted to please her. So they carried on thus for a while and she soon became hot again. They began to kiss repeatedly and increased the tempo of their orgy. Faster and faster they moved, faster and faster. She was again as before – a prisoner in the grip of a ferocious passion. She soon came to her second climax and his cock began to swim in a boiling sea.

'I'm going to come pretty soon,' he cried enthusiastically. 'I feel it. Work with me a little longer, sweetheart.'

'All right, you wonderful lover. Come, come! Oh, please come.' She slapped his back and ass in a frenzy of delight and she made her cunt and legs as tight as possible. His tool worked with the speed and regularity of a piston, and at last the longed-for Stream of Eros came, jetting into her womb like liquid fire. They clasped each other tempestuously and kissed as the throbbing of his penis ebbed away.

They lay a little while in a daze and then parted.

'Oh, but you were splendid,' she breathed hoarsely.

'I made you come twice, didn't I,' he chuckled. 'And you kidded me about not knowing my business.'

'I was merely chaffing,' she laughed.

He got up and looked in the wardrobe. He found his watch. 'Gee! It's almost six o'clock. I've got to go.'

'Oh, surely not,' she cried. 'I must have you once more. Don't go yet, please.'

'But gee,' he remonstrated, 'I had two pieces before I came to see you. It would take too long to have another piece.'

'I'll suck it for you,' she suggested.

'All right – but we'll have to work fast. I've got a lot to do between now and eight.'

They washed their privates and she bade him lie on his back. Then she sat beside him, and bending down, took his limp cock in her mouth and gave it a tongue massage. He stared, fascinated at the spectacle of his tool between her lovely red lips, and she was so dainty about it, as though it were the accepted thing to do. Slowly but surely his member began to rise, and to stiffen it further, she moved up and down on it, using her lips as a vulva. At times he could feel the head of it in her throat. During all this he was fingering her cunt very vigorously.

Finally he gave her to know that he was ready for action. She withdrew her lips regretfully and he got up while she assumed her proper position. They fucked again, and a pleasurable bout it was, lasting many minutes, both coming almost as one. They washed, and with arrangements to meet again and endearing kisses, he got his clothes on and left.

II

An Oxford Thesis on Love

LUPTON WILKINSON 1938

The year 1938 saw the appearance of a classic of American erotic fiction, *An Oxford Thesis on Love*. It became so famous and legendary that it served as a model for a long series of erotic tales over the next decade that have collectively come to be known as 'The Oxford Professor' series.

G. Legman, dean of living erotobibliographers, has identified Lupton Wilkinson, a Hollywood writer of British origin, as the author of the original *Oxford Thesis*. The eight separate pieces comprising the work seem to have been written on consignment for Roy Johnson, an Oklahoma oil millionaire who, claiming to have already read all the printed English-language erotica, started to pay for new manuscripts for his reading pleasure. The new texts reached him through 'agents' in various cities such as Chicago, Los Angeles and New York. Wily authors, or their agents, soon realised that extra money could be earned if carbons of the manuscripts were made and sold or rented to other customers.

One can only conjecture what specifically Roy Johnson requested. The author though makes his purpose quite clear. The title page of his book states in full: '*An Oxford Thesis on Love*. In which L. Erectus Mentulus, PH.D., late fellow of Oxford College, draws from his various experiences for the instruction, entertainment and greater zest of his colleagues, friends and admirers. *Tot feminae, quot cunni – qualis cunnus, talis amor*. One Hundred Copies Done Into A Book By The Hand Of The Author. Taos, New Mexico, May 1938.'

Wilkinson further elucidates his intentions on the following page: '*An Oxford Thesis on Love*. Being a series of diverting and edifying dialogues in which it is conclusively shown that fornication is not as simple as it has frequently been considered, that different gates present different vistas and that all women are not the same; profusely illuminated with physical, biological and metaphysical analogies culled by the author from numerous beds, sofas, chairs and floors both in this and foreign climes, and sprinkled with his advice and suggestions as to proper bed procedure and concluding with a bout guaranteed to be unique in the long annals of the pubic war.'

The first printed appearance of *An Oxford Thesis on Love* was strange indeed. It consisted of one hundred and twenty-three sheets of paper each $8^{1}/_{2}$" x 11" with mimeoed text on one side only. It was sewn together with cord, and illustrated with a coloured frontis and twelve explicit silver-print photographs which were glued to black construction paper and randomly inserted into the text before binding. A forward by the author best explains the trials of producing the volume: 'An Experiment In Book Making. Ever greater are the obstacles thrown in the path of a publisher attempting to issue a volume dealing with the facts of life as it is lived; the authorities remain stubbornly infantile in their crusading psychosis. When, therefore, the author, urged by his intimates to make his Thesis available to a wider circle of colleagues and friends, found no printer available who would risk all, he determined to do the book himself. This volume is the result. Mimeographing paraphernalia [*sic*] was rented. Stencils were typed on the machine which had served so well for the labour of composition. Photographs were printed in a cellar darkroom from negatives in the author's files or generously posed by lovely collaborators. The lithograph was pulled in the art department of a friendly college, but coloured in the safer confines of the author's study. The binding was a stint indeed. Only the slip case was commercially manufactured; a nearby match factory obliged. May this effort justify the hours of toil that were put into it.'

To this detailed description we can add little. Emile Ganzo was probably the artist, and his lithograph printed in New York's Art Student League. While possibly written in Taos, the book was produced in New York.

What makes *An Oxford Thesis on Love* special? On the surface it would seem to be a pedantic exposition, which although urbane and sophisticated, would not have much popular interest. Seriousness always seems to take the fun out of an erotic story, ruining any 'turn on' the text might have. In addition there was a plethora of academic sexological books available, authored by individuals with scientific credentials, for those readers wishing serious discussions of erotic subjects. What makes *An Oxford Thesis on Love* special is its implicit humour.

The theoretical postulations of the narrator, a British professor, take place not in a college auditorium or at the podium of a lecture hall, but in a back booth of Dave's Soft-Drink Emporium, located not in a university town, but in rural America, a place one expects in Thornton Wilder's *Our Town* or Meredith Wilson's *Music Man*. The professor's audience consists not of fellow academicians of like serious intent, but of a barber, a druggist and a travelling salesman, all with the same thing in common – sex on the brain! The book's entertainment comes not only from the sexual descriptions, but the mixing of plain and fancy. The high formality of the language used on so 'low' a subject renders all seriousness mock.

The Oxford professor's audience in the book, and reading the book, may be sceptical of his erudition, but are fascinated by what he says, and entertained by how he says it. Wilkinson may have meant his text to be a totally serious thesis of sexological importance on the vagaries of sexual intercourse, but fortunately it turned out otherwise. Moreover, his book served as the impetus for the hilarious sexual satires of other authors trying to capitalise on the success of the first Oxford Professor book. 'But that,' as the professor himself would say, 'is another story.'

Here then is an excerpt . . .

from *An Oxford Thesis on Love*

It was the salesman who started the conversation by enquiring about the similarity of sisters and particularly twins as to bed technique.

'It's been your point, I believe,' he said 'that no two women fuck the same way. I'll admit that the instances you have described have all been different But how about twins? When they look, talk and almost think alike, don't they screw the same?'

'There are no reduplications in nature. Even identical twins are not identical, and Lorine and Lorette were as near alike as the nipples on your girl's breasts. Their temperaments were not quite so alike. Lorine was quieter, with a slow, warm sense of humour, while Lorette was lively and possessed of high animal spirits. They were of medium height, with golden hair and firm, neat figures, so similar that the parts might have been interchangeable.'

'Were they really acrobats?' the barber asked.

They were tumblers, playing in Vienna for a two-month engage-
ment and they stayed at my pension in Tegethofstrasse. The fact that
we were all Americans drew us together somewhat, and we soon grew
quite friendly. I was particularly drawn to Lorine, whose soft friendly
smile I found engaging. Not that I didn't like Lorette, but I always tend
to be somewhat reserved with girls who are too vivacious.

At the girls' eager invitation I attended a performance on which they
were billed with their troupe. I have never been much amused by
acrobats, but I found my two friends to be cute. They were dressed in
white dresses with short, flaring skirts that hit them high on their
muscular but attractive thighs. When they bent over in various forma-
tions they revealed white panties stretched tightly over firm little
bottoms. Identical as they seemed, I felt my gaze attracted always to
Lorine and began to consider how I could manage to secure her favours.

Some of their acts were to play a part in my further relations with
them, so I will now describe them. The 'Tower of Babel' was one of
those ridiculous conceptions so frequently found on the variety stage.
The whole troupe piled one after the other on top of each other, the
largest on the bottom, the next resting on hands and knees atop him,
and so on. On the very top of the pile rested Lorine and Lorette. For a
moment this living pile remained motionless. Then Lorette, letting her
knees and arms fall astraddle of Lorine, fell flat against her back.
Lorine repeated the movement and so the whole pillar seemed to
collapse on itself until it was but a fraction of its previous height. Then
began a slow oscillation which ended by the tumbling off, one by one,
of the performers until the 'Tower' was in ruins.

Another simple but, as it proved, fruitful trick was accomplished by
the twins together. Twining their legs around each other they rolled
down a high incline and over a shorter one, the acceleration of their
descent carrying them on. It was delightful to watch them rolling in a
flurry of skirts and legs, with hair waving and bottoms flashing.

After this, I began to pay marked attention to Lorine, to whom I was
particularly attracted. Our rooms being adjacent promised to facilitate
matters later, but the fact that the twins were practically inseparable
raised present difficulties. I knew that Lorine liked me, but I could
hardly make love to her in Lorette's presence. At last, however, a
threatened cold kept Lorette confined to her room and Lorine
promised to go picnicking with me in the Wienerwald.

We set out in high spirits and with a determination on my part not to
return until I had tasted to the full the hidden pleasures of my

companion's body. I slackened my pace from time to time and, falling back, watched the firm swing of her legs under the short hiking skirt. I felt that the man for whom she spread them would not soon forget the experience.

Not until we had eaten our lunch did I make any advance. Then, stretched out under the tall oak trees, I took her in my arms and kissed her. She gave me her lips readily enough, allowing me to tongue her and returning the caress with facility. Encouraged by this, I felt of her breasts and began to unfasten her shirtwaist. She made no protest, indeed helped me at last to expose both of her small, tight boobies.

'Are they too small for your taste?' she asked as I ran my hands over their smooth curves. 'Wouldn't you like to have them big and round and soft so you could squeeze them?'

'I love them as they are,' I assured her. 'Small teats have a charm all their own. Spiritually, there's a firmness and honesty about them that is beautiful; physically, my hands tremble joyfully over their rolling curves and my tongue loves the titillation of small nipples.'

As I said this I applied my mouth gently to one teat and licked my tongue rapidly across the nipple. Bending back as it was rubbed against my tongue, it slowly came erect, while its twin stiffened enviously. At last, my tongue growing tired, I took one of her breasts in the palm of my hand and began to shake it. At this she sighed with pleasure and, leaning her head back, closed her eyes.

You are familiar with the advisability of arousing the passion of your partner before mounting her, but what is not sufficiently emphasised is the complementary effect on the man. To watch the growing heat of the woman whom you know you are soon to fuck is one of the most delightful sensations that I know of. This is not, of course, a rule without exceptions. Jane of the Bouncing Bottom, for example, was a creature I loved to serve without warning. I was particularly fond of getting my penis out and erect without her knowledge and suddenly pulling her down on the floor, driving it in her and, before she had guessed what I was about, starting to screw her. But small, tender-fleshed girls like Lorine should be slowly and lovingly aroused to passion. It is lovely to watch their virginal bodies bending to the gusts of emotion that your hands bring to them. And, as you watch them, your own desires are heightened and focused.

Lorine's face was flushed and her breath coming in short pants when the soft froufrou of cloth caused me to glance down. She was shaking her bottom in slow, regular movements that followed the movement of my hand on her breast. As I pushed her teat up, her buttocks arched;

when I pushed down, her buttocks came down. I increased the speed with which I was caressing her paps, and her ass began to work convulsively.

I at once realised that I had to do with a comparatively rare but delightful type. Many girls are so affected by booby play as to shake their asses, but such perfect synchronisation is an almost infallible sign of what I have named the 'grace-note fuckers'. Knoikow, in his otherwise excellent work, *Cunt Hunting among the Virgin Thighs*, makes the absurd error of classing such girls among the 'virgin women' and insisting that they are incapable of securing an orgasm in the normal manner. In my review of his book for the *Ladies' Monthly*, I pointed out a sharp differentiation. Grace-note fuckers are perfectly normal, but are so susceptible that their first orgasm comes very quickly and without the need for actual insertion. For a short time after this, they are exhausted and unwilling to entertain the advances of their partner, who is by now burning with eagerness. As a result, he either screws her against her will or leaves her convinced that she is a mere cock-teaser. This is unfair; had he but given her a little time, she would have been ready to offer him a piece of ass that he would not forget for a long time.

Ready to give Lorine first satisfaction, I reached down and pulled up her dress. To my astonishment, she was wearing no undies at all, but at once displayed to my admiring eyes the most intimate treasures of her love-pocket. The light golden hair which grew upward towards her belly was already damp; her motions, which had grown slower but not ceased when I released her breasts, arched her body rhythmically. At these moments the lips of her cunt were pressed open and revealed the damp pink flesh of her vagina.

'Don't put it in me yet, Lee,' she begged, realising that the sight of her shaking privies must seem a complete invitation. 'I'll give you all you want, but not yet.'

'That's all right, dear,' I told her. 'I know what you want.'

I lowered myself between her legs until I was bent over her cunt and, bending over, pressed my lips for a moment to the hair-fringed slit. Her breath whistled through her teeth with pleasure at this intimate contact. When I lifted my head, she arched her back desperately in the wild attempt to raise her cunt to my lips. Her knees were bent at right angles, her thighs spread open so wide that she seemed nearly split in two, and her dress hung from her waist as she lifted her bottom more than a foot from the ground in pursuit of another genital kiss.

'Don't tease me,' she begged. 'Suck me off. Run your tongue in my hole. Please, please.'

Touched by the madness of her voice, I threw myself upon her and pressed my lips to the sticky crevice, sucking her toit between my lips, running my tongue along the hairy slit or plunging it as far as I could into her hole itself. She, on her side, kept her ass in constant motion, pressing up against me and forcing her toit so open that I was able to insert my lips in her joy-cup, or roughing my cheeks with her pubic hair and smearing my mouth with the moisture of her passion. Her fanny was generally off the ground, and I slipped my hands between her open thighs and clutched her buttocks. My thumbs caressed the sensitive portion between cunthole and asshole, while my fingers ran smoothly over her small, firm butts.

In a voice broken with passion, she gave me directions.

'Suck hard,' she would beg. Or: 'Run your tongue in and out of my hole. I'm almost coming.'

At last she seized my head in her hands and pressed it between her legs until I was almost suffocated. I renewed the fervour of my caresses, however, and was soon rewarded by the reception of a rich orgasm, which filled my lips and trickled down my chin.

She pushed me away at last and lay exhausted, her dress wrinkled up under her arms, her naked legs still bent and opened, shamelessly revealing her whole hairy toit, to which still clung the pearly drops of her orgasm. The sight nearly drove me mad with desire and I was strongly tempted to mount her at once. But I controlled myself, knowing that a little patience now would be more than repaid later.

At last she opened her eyes and looked at me with glowing eyes. 'Lee, you're so wonderful, to go down on me and then give me time to recover.'

Her glance fell to where my dick was wildly trying to free itself from confinement.

'Poor boy,' she said, 'you're burning up. Will it help you to wait if I pull down my dress?' And she made as if to cover her nakedness. I hurriedly assured her that my torment was a pleasure as long as I could feast my eyes on the spring which was to end it.

'Do you like it?' she asked, coyly curling a damp strand of hair around her finger. 'Do you know,' she continued when I had expressed my admiration, 'that I purposely didn't wear undies because I was intending to give you everything you wanted? I suppose you'll think I'm a regular bitch, but I've been as hot as you for the past week. Once or twice, when I could see your dick raising his head in your trousers, it was almost as much as I could do to keep from throwing myself on you.'

This revelation so stirred me that I immediately released my prick and made as if to mount her. She begged me to wait, however, and I finally lay back while she stroked my staff with gentle fingers.

'You're the only man who was ever patient like this,' she said. 'The others would pay no attention to my pleas, but insisted on putting it right in me. And then they were always mad because I was so cold and passive. I promise, however, that I'll be so hot for you that you'll scarcely hold me. Your cock is so white and sweet. I love it.'

When she said this, she leaned over and kissed it. This was more than I could stand and, seizing her head between my hands, I plunged the full length in her mouth. For a moment she was almost choked, but soon recovering, she began to suck me with skill and enthusiasm. For a while she would mouth the head, caressing it with her tongue; then she would take it all in her mouth until her lips were tugging the hairs around the base. Then she released it slowly, her lips clinging damply to it until it slipped out with a loud smack.

I was fast approaching the danger point when she suddenly released my cock and looked up with flushed face and burning eyes.

'I'm ready for it now, Lee,' she gasped. 'Put it up me, quick.'

I rolled over on top of her and her eager fingers quickly guided my cock into her anxious hole. Though obviously not a virgin, she had a tight little cunt that clutched me firmly and rubbed with every thrust. Her fanny was in constant motion as she shook it up and down or rolled from side to side; occasionally she arched her back and, lifting her ass clear off the ground, held me aloft. At such times I clutched her buttocks in my hands and found the firm flesh, tightened with tension, to be like warm ivory.

'I've never been so hot before,' she admitted. 'Let me get on top of you.'

Without waiting for my answer, she tightened her arms around me and rolled me over. For a moment, as we rolled, my prick came partly out; then, as her full weight came down on me, her hole engulfed it and her belly jammed tightly against mine. The next minute, she elevated her ass until only the head of my cock was in her. In this position she bent her head until she could look back and see our privies while she slowly worked her bottom up and down.

'I love to watch it go in and out of me,' she giggled.

The titillation at the end of my cock was more than I could stand. In particular, the rough caress of her toit hair maddened me and, arching my own back, I drove the full length into her again. But my knees were too close together and my movement threw me off balance. For a moment we tottered – then rolled over again with me once more on top.

Now, we had not selected our spot with due consideration for the vagaries of a professional tumbler. This second lunge had carried us to the edge of a gently sloping, sodded hill, and an unusually lusty bounce by Lorine carried us over the incline. With a cry, half of fear and half of delight, Lorine wrapped her legs about me and we were rolling downhill, cheek to cheek and privies tightly together.

To a spectator, our descent would, I suppose, have appeared ridiculous, had his interest not been aroused by the naked legs of Lorine, her billowing skirts and the frequent sight of her white buttocks glowing in the light like a full moon. To me, once the first astonishment and fright had passed, the trip was one of delirious ecstasy. The slope was gentle and our comparatively slow progress was softened by my companion's skill, so I was enabled to enjoy to the full the pubic sensations aroused by this novel means of perambulating fornication.

Unless you are able to visualise the successive positions we occupied, gentlemen, you will not be able successfully to follow my description. I should really have such a model as is used to demonstrate the movements of the stars – a sort of genital planetarium. As a matter of fact, when I was an exchange professor at the University of Delhi, I constructed a series of lantern slides to use in describing this novel intercourse to my graduate class in Main Currents in Western Fucking. Unfortunately, the slides were later stolen by a colleague in the Department of Buggery, who believed the position could be duplicated in his own field.

But let us see if I can describe matters in words. As I would roll over from my position on top, the base of my cock would be pressed more and more tightly against one side of her cunt, while it was at the same time bent in a fashion that another time I would have thought painful. As I slipped on my side, a few inches eased out of her, only to be plunged violently back as she came on top. And this forward plunge was quite different to the ordinary drive, in which the head touches nothing. The angle of insertion was such that my penis was driven against the side of her vagina, down which it slid. The sensation was maddeningly intense. I can describe it only by comparing it to that experienced when a woman lets her teeth clutch the shaft of your penis while her tongue presses against the head. I could not have stood it had it not been instantly followed by a complete insertion as her fanny gleamed in the light and she took the saddle. The next moment, as she was rolling off, my prick was bent in the other direction and one side of her cunt rubbed it roughly as her hole gave up part of its prize.

All of these diverse pressures and contacts succeeded each other with such rapidity as to blend into a bewildering tactual whole. Halfway down, I felt my excitement mounting to a climax, and a moment later, as Lorine rolled over a little mount and pressed me unusually tightly, I repaid her with a jet of semen. From that point to our final halt on the level ground, my tightened balls pumped a shot in her every time her ass touched the ground. Her own orgasm, as she later told me, began with the second dose and continued until we lay quiet with me on top.

When we finally recovered enough to disengage, we discovered that we were sore and tired. Lorine, while in better condition than I, had been unprotected by clothes. Rolling over on her stomach, she showed me her bottom, which was bruised by stones and scratched by twigs. I pressed a kiss on each of the solid little buttocks before allowing her to pull down her dress.

'If you'll unlock the door between our rooms, I'll come in tonight after Lorette's asleep,' she promised as we started home. 'Having discovered what a passionate little bitch I am, you'll be surprised to learn that Lorette's a virgin – and, what's more, thinks I am. We must be careful not to let her know that you're laying me. I don't know how it would affect her.'

I expressed surprise that twins should be so different, and Lorine admitted that she also found it astonishing.

'I suppose it's a matter of still waters running deep,' she said. 'Lorette's always kidding and petting, but she only goes so far. Now, I don't dare pet. If a man just squeezes a teat, I go all soft and he can do everything he wants to with me, if he doesn't make the mistake of not waiting till I come the first time.'

At eleven I heard the twins getting ready to go to bed in their room. I took off my clothes, so as to be ready, and waited for Lorine's arrival. As the minutes passed, I became more and more impatient, but at last the door swung open and a white figure in a nightgown slipped through and quickly closed it behind her. She fell into my arms with a sigh of delight and I could feel her body trembling under the thin muslin of her nightgown. I drew her to the bed and, stripping her nightgown over her head, tumbled her into the huge German feather bed.

Once more I relieved her first hot transports by going down on her. In a short while, my eager lips had reduced her to panting satisfaction and we lay, half buried in the soft mattress, waiting till she recovered sufficiently for a real fuck.

'Do you believe in mental telepathy?' she asked me suddenly.

Surprised at such an inappropriate remark, I explained that the phenomenon was beyond question.

'Twins,' I continued, 'are particularly good subjects. It is as if they were mentally attuned. There are innumerable instances of one twin being aware of an accident to the other at the very instant at which it occurs.'

Lorine looked at me with big eyes.

'It's happened to us several times,' she said. 'But something happened today that never occurred before. I told you that Lorette has no suspicion that my maidenhead is not as intact as her own. Well, she had an experience this afternoon that would have given me away had she been less trusting.'

'What do you mean?' I asked.

'She was asleep when she began to have a vivid dream. She thought that a huge, naked man was kneeling over her with his hands on her thighs. She couldn't see his face, but, as he touched her, she felt her legs spreading open despite her efforts to keep them together. And as her legs opened, his penis, which had been limp, quickly came erect and swelled to a huge size. The sight of this erection filled her with a tremendous excitement, and, though she was afraid, she felt an overwhelming desire to have him put it in her. She hurriedly pulled up her nightgown and, seizing the man's cock in her hand, pushed it into her hole. The pleasure of this entry was so great that she awoke laughing with pleasure. Her nightie was wrinkled up under her arms, and her cunt was wet.'

'Perhaps it was just an erotic dream,' I ventured.

'Lorette doesn't have them. Besides, this occurred at three-thirty. She looked at the clock.'

I murmured my astonishment. This was about the time that I had first driven my penis into Lorine's cunt.

'You're afraid that Lorette will put two and two together sometime and realise that her dreams are merely the psychic shadow of what you are experiencing?'

'I'm afraid she might. I almost didn't come tonight for fear she'd wake up and, finding me gone, know what was up.'

'But you did come.'

She smiled at me and I could see that passion and desire had crept back in her face. 'I kept thinking of you sitting in here, all white and naked, and I imagined how stiff and big the old boy would be, and I simply had to come in and get it.'

I took her in my arms and rolled between her legs. The thought that, as I pressed it in her, Lorette in the next room might in her sleep be spreading her own legs for the ghostly attack of a phantom cock was exciting. It was as if I were fucking two girls in different rooms at the same time.

Lorine must have read my thoughts, for she laughed at me as I began to screw my prick around in her.

'I hope your dream self gives sister as hot a time as you're giving me,' she said.

But my dream self had to look out for himself. The marvellous fuck that Lorine proceeded to give me was too exciting to permit me to think of anything else. I dare say you have thought that I had forgotten to compare Lorine to other women from the customary back position. I have with Lorine been following our chronological order, but am now ready to make good my observations.

As her privies got hotter and hotter under the plunging, rolling thrusts of my dick, Lorine began to arch her back. Her action was as instinctive as the reaching of a child for a bright object. She couldn't endure the loss, even for a second, of one inch of my cock, and kept raising her bottom higher and higher, like Oliver Twist holding out his bowl for more. Soon her buttocks were clear of the bed and I was being raised aloft. Remembering the afternoon's experience and not wishing to be rolled off the bed, I attempted to press her down again. I might as well have tried to push down an auto jack. Tumbling hardens the muscles, and Lorine's thighs and buttocks were living steel. And so it was that I soon found myself held a good foot off the bed, supported by her taut belly and the tips of my toes. In this position I was unable to secure a point of leverage, and my prick, pushed tightly in her, was unable to move.

But Lorine more than made up for my enforced passivity. With bent, opened legs, she kept us safely in position while her shaking, bouncing ass tossed me to and fro like a cork. Relaxing one leg somewhat, she would give a violent thrust with the other thigh and so roll me to one side, partly withdrawing my penis, which was rudely rubbed against one side of her slit. As I was on the verge of falling over, the other leg would toss me back again, reversing the process and plunging me in her so deep that I felt as if my very balls were about to be forced up her.

It was another type of ass technique, however, that finally brought on an orgasm. With tightened legs, she would hold me aloft like an athlete preparing for action, and then, with a tremendous thrust of her trained muscles, she would toss me several inches up in the air and catch me, so to speak, with another thrust upward as I dropped back. The sensation of being tossed almost out of her hole, followed by the shocking impact as it was driven back in, was more than my penis could endure. I could feel my orgasm approaching and, unable to do anything for myself, I begged her to continue until I was relieved.

A moment later, as our bellies slapped together, the first jet of semen was jerked out of me as one shakes ink from a pen. Again and again, as our bodies plunged together, my love-juice was taken from me in this fashion. I seemed to have no control over its ejection, and my cock paid tribute to a series of delicious assailments.

Just before the last drop was taken, Lorine, who had been showing signs of increasing excitement, cried out that she was coming. At the same moment, her legs gave way and she fell back on the bed – with my prick following her cunt.

We lay quiet for several minutes. That is, I did. Lorine occasionally writhed and twitched as her fanny responded to a particularly intense shock of satisfied passion. A half-hour later she quietly slipped back into her room. I glanced in after her to see if Lorette had been awakened.

Lorette was still asleep, but I saw at once that my ghost had not been inactive. A streetlight dimly illuminated the room, and I could see my mistress's twin quite plainly. The cover was tossed off her, her nightgown was drawn up under her arms, and her widely spread, naked legs were stretched out on the mattress. In the faint light I could just make out the damp mat of hair between her legs, which occasionally twitched. Lorine, seeing me watching, hurriedly covered her sister's naked charms and motioned me back. I closed the door and went back to bed.

'And did Lorette ever learn about her sister?' the druggist enquired.

The professor looked at his watch.

'I hadn't realised it would take me so long to tell about Lorine,' he said. 'It's too late now for me to tell you about the "Tower of Babel". I'll have to continue the story at our next meeting. You'll find the answers to all your questions then.'

'Well, I hope you did more for Lorette than ghost-fuck her,' the salesman said. 'I call it a lousy trick to play on a virgin.'

~ 12 ~

The Passionate Pedant

G. LEGMAN *et al.* 1939

Lupton Wilkinson's *An Oxford Thesis of Love* was so popular, that there was an instant call for more of this wonderfully burlesque 1938 erotica. It is not hard to figure out why. That work was funny, sexy, and exceptionally well written, certainly an unbeatable combination, as the history of erotica will corroborate.

Erotic literature and comedy have had a long and mutually beneficial association. Whether as social satire, character assassination or pure bawdry, explicit sexual descriptions have figured prominently in humour. What is more slapstick than someone caught in an embarrassing sexual situation? No wonder there is an entire genre know simply as 'sex comedy' or 'sex farce'. Pornographic graffiti, for the most part pretty hilarious, predates literature itself. It is said that seven eighths of all the really good jokes are 'dirty', as are one hundred per cent of all the worthwhile limericks. One can only guess how far back in prehistory lie the origins of erotic humour in the oral tradition. After all, ancient Greek and Roman artifacts with oversized genitalia still today elicit a smile or chuckle. For written literature in English we need only remember Shakespeare's bawdy, *double-entendre* asides, while the Earl of Rochester's *Sodom* (1684) was in its entirety an obscene political play, drawing heavily on erotic punning and sexual satire. The Victorian erotic periodical *The Pearl* devoted a large part of its text to sexually explicit jokes, riddles, limericks, and humorous verse. The Edwardian *Pleasure Bound* series of pornographic novels even included ethnic (Yiddish!) comedy. Oriental erotica of the last thousand years was steeped in a culturally distinct humour, whether it be a Chinese novel such as the *Chin Ping Mei* or any of a number of Japanese pillow and wood-block books. In fact, the psychological nature of humour being what it is, it is difficult to find any erotic or pornographic story that does not have some comedy in it.

The literature of the United States also has a rich history of erotic humour. There are the endless jokes and parodies and verse that filled such classic American twentieth-century erotic anthologies as *Immortalia* (1927) or *Anecdota Americana* (1927 & 1932), as well as (in)famous nineteenth-century examples like Eugene Field's short poem *Little Willie* and Mark Twain's sexy farce *1601*. There is even eighteenth-century American sexual humour by the likes of Ben Franklin! Yet it took Lupton Wilkinson to author a full-length book that was humorous and burlesque in a purely American idiom.

With a public clamour for more, and an obvious buck to be made, the people responsible for the publication of Wilkinson's *An Oxford Thesis on Love* once again put into print some of the erotica that had originally been privately commissioned by Oklahoma millionaire Roy Johnson, but authored by other pens as Wilkinson became otherwise occupied in Hollywood. Hence in 1939 there appeared 'The Passionate Pedant: Being a New Oxford Thesis on Love', wherein L. Erectus Mentulus, late of Oxford, establishes incontrovertibly that the sexual enjoyment of women of divers races is evocative of distinctly different types and degrees of pleasure, through narratives of his own experience, with particular emphasis upon psycho-physiological adumbrations *et cetera*, for the entertainment as well as the enlightenment of his friends. *In Cunnis diversis – voluptates diversae*. Done By The Hand Of The Author Into A Manuscript At Oshkosh, Wisconsin, September 1939.' Same as the year before, the place of printing was actually the basement of the Chrysler Building in New York City. Like *An Oxford Thesis* this book was 8½" x 11" with mimeoed text on one side of the page only. The publisher was a bit more sophisticated this time around. The pages were actually glued into a folded wrapper (rather that crudely sewn as before), and the 104 pages were illustrated with five hand-coloured erotic plates. The book consisted of four separate stories, set respectively in Japan, Malaya, Mozambique and Hungary.

Once more we have the professor regaling middle America with his scholarly lectures on sex around the world. While he may be trying, or pretending, to be academic, what he is really dishing out is pure porn. Couched in pseudopedagogical language and structure, with numerous references and footnotes to arcane (and frequently fictitious) tomes of sexual knowledge, the humour often-times reads like *borscht*-belt comedy.

The stories though are all good 'dirty' fun. They are not malicious or forced. The characters are uninhibited, lusty, but genuinely human and caring. For them, male and female, sex is an end unto itself. A roll in the hay (literally, in one of the tales) is as acceptable an evening's entertainment as say going to a movie show, or the Emporium for an ice-cream soda. And the tales are exotic, the action occurring in far off places, known to most of the audience only through *National Geographic*.

What made and has kept these stories so popular is that there is more to them than mere farce. Those in the know quickly realise that they do contain among all the foolery a great deal of accurate and esoteric information about numerous cultures from around the world, especially as pertains to sexual customs. Whether it is reference to the 'Hottentot apron' or the Japanese slang word for 'vagina', it is clear that the authors were not of average life experience. Their extraordinary knowledge is displayed not only as boastful show, but as an integral part of the erotic humour – the plain and fancy juxtaposition.

Although, as previously noted, the various Oxford Professor tales over the years came to be by different pens, there were certain common denominators in all of them. Burlesque humour was the major unifying theme; broad sexual humour and explicit erotic descriptions delivered in pedantic and pedagogical format. There was the repeated play of plain and fancy language as characters joyfully lusted through life with no dire consequences, and their amorous activities were told with numerous *double entendres* and puns of rather creative imagination. The constant introduction of esoteric and arcane sexual ethno-anthropological information, reminiscent of, or satirising, the weighty turn-of-the-century scholarly tomes of this genre by the likes of Drs Ploss & Bartels, Dr Jacobus X, Dr Ivan Bloch and Professor Friedrich Krauss, presented with lexicographical pomposity and not a few totally fictitious facts and figures, made these tales unlike any that had ever before appeared in the American erotica market. In the extreme what chronically appeared on the page was nothing more than the highest levels of technical social science reduced to sexual slang and four-letter words. But it was fun, and that was the point, as the formal, academic, scholarly and scientific mien of the writing was the perfect foil to accentuate the real nature of the text – hot tales of fancy fucking!

Here then is an excerpt . . .

〜 from *The Passionate Pedant*

'Well, gentlemen,' said the professor, 'we are gathered once again to discuss cunt in its socio-psychological significance in modern civilisation. I would suggest that an infusion of some vinous reagent might help materially in bringing us to the proper point of scientific impersonality.' He broke off and looked significantly at the barber, who was fussing with the wine bottle. The barber looked blank, but the druggist nudged him and nodded toward the bottle.

'Oh, yes, indeed,' prompted the druggist. 'A little scientific reagent.'

'Yeh, sure. I get it,' the barber said, pouring drinks all around. 'Scientific impersonality – we need lots of that.'

'A word to the wine is sufficient,' the travelling salesman contributed.

The professor frowned at the salesman – he disliked puns – and took a careful sip of his wine. Satisfied with its flavour and bouquet, he, too, downed it.

'I must admit,' he said, after staring pensively at his glass for a few moments, 'that I do not precisely remember what it was that I promised to discuss at this meeting . . .'

'You were going to tell us about the different races, and how the women were different,' volunteered the barber hastily.

'Ah, yes. Yes, so I was,' mused the professor. 'The women of different races. And an interesting subject it is, indeed. To begin with, it must be remembered that there are five main races of mankind, not to mention womankind – namely, the white, yellow, brown, black and red. And you may believe me when I say that the women of each of these are quite divergent tidbits of eroticism.

'Aside from the direct pigmentational distinctions, there are, of course, numerous nationalities – some eight or nine hundred in all, in point of fact – the women of each and every one of which differ erotically in greater or lesser degree.

'Physically, of course, they are all very much alike, or, more correctly, the personal differences of a simply anatomical nature are rather the same in all races, with a few notable exceptions.'

'Sure,' interrupted the salesman, 'like Japanese women – their cunts are slanted, sort of.'

The professor looked pained and sighed disgustedly before answering the untoward interruption. 'Very interesting, I am sure,' he said, 'but, unfortunately, merely an ignorant superstition.

'Approaching the question directly, among the twenty-seven hundred Chinese and Japanese women examined by Niklucho in compiling statistics for his book *The Alleged Obliquity of the Sino-Japanese Cunt*, not one cunt was encountered that showed even the slightest declination from the perpendicular.

'Further, from numerous experiences with women of both these races, I am in a position to state that there is no truth whatsoever in this belief. Major Vyvyan Blystone Knott VC, suggested in the masterly appendix to his *Peregrinations of a Pensive Prick*, which appeared anonymously many years ago, and which has never been superseded, that this belief was originally just a joke, and that by repetition to persons ignorant of the facts, the jocular origin was forgotten and the belief that the Oriental vulva is diagonally placed came to be considered factual.'

'Yeh, I guess maybe you're right, professor,' the salesman said. 'After all, I never had any personal experience with a chink or a Jap.'

'I am right,' the professor insisted a bit superciliously, 'and I have had such personal experience.

'I was merely saying,' the professor continued, 'that, with certain notable exceptions in particular races, a cunt is a cunt all over the world. That is, in its physical conformation, although certain details such as colouring and the odour and flavour of the cunt juice differ slightly according to race. The large exceptions are in the cases of such racial peculiarities as the so-called Hottentot apron, by which I mean only the natural hyperelongation of the inner lips of the cunt and not any ritual mutilations in this way.

'The Hottentot apron is actually found in certain tribes of the Hottentots in central Africa, and in some cases the inner lips hang halfway down to the knees, requiring that they be spread apart with the hands before it is possible to fuck the lady in question.

'Elongations of this sort are occasionally met with among women even of the Caucasian race – a fact not particularly well-known – particularly in brunettes. I have myself encountered two such cases, one a seamstress in southern Bavaria and the other a salesgirl in Des Moines.

'The only other vulvula peculiarity that I can think of offhand is extremely long hair on the pubes. There is not any geographical delimitation of this peculiarity, and I have myself found it in the white, yellow and brown races, and have seen it recorded as having occurred in the black. The red race is not extremely hirsute in any respect, and I do not doubt but that this particular peculiarity is quite unknown among them.

'However, I can no doubt describe the various types of women and their racial traits more expeditiously by telling you of my rather intriguing experiences with them rather than by speaking of them impersonally. I shall tell you first, as has been suggested, of my experiences with Oriental women. I have in mind one pretty little geisha whom I shall call Osukima.

'In Japan a geisha must be pretty – as Oriental standards of prettiness go – and well educated. She must be a brilliant conversationalist, a superb dancer, a musician and an erotic artist. Her price is high, very high, but she is well worth it. The sad thing about the institution of the geisha is that she herself receives little of the rewards of her charms. Most of the money is taken by the mistress of the house.

'Osukima was simply a pretty little geisha who had but lately gone through her novitiate of training and entered an establishment as a full-fledged geisha. This was in Osaka, where I had gone to study the collection of erotic art in the secret archives of the great University of Osaka. My teacher, Utare Yamaguchi, the famous author of several treatises on coital posture and technique – none of which, unfortunately, have been translated – introduced me to many of the military attachés who are invariably present in Japan at the behest of foreign governments that, having taught Japan the arts of war, are now afraid of what the pupil is doing with its newfound knowledge.

'These fellows, ranking officers all of them, were pleasant companions, if a bit 'horsey', and, more important to the present tale, were *personae gratae* in all the better establishments in the Yoshiwara of Osaka. Through them I had entrée therein and spent innumerable pleasant evenings listening to the plaintive music and watching the graceful dances of the geishas.

'Thus I met Osukima. "Suki", she said simply and with downcast eyes when I asked her what her name was.

'Suki played the *samisen* for me and danced when I bade her dance for me. She gave me tidbits to eat from her lips and whispered inflammatory nothings in my ear in a combination of Japanese and Pidgin English. I was much taken by her and called for her every evening. You must not think, gentlemen, that men go to the Yoshiwara only to be fucked. A house of geishas is a combination bar, club and cabaret. One goes there to drink, to dine, to play Go, the Oriental form of chess, and to discuss the affairs of the world.

'It was more than two weeks after I had first been attended by Suki that I fucked her. I had been conserving my penile energy during that time in pursuing an affair I was having with the wife of one of the French attachés, a lovely little blonde Parisienne whose military husband made the tactical blunder of serving his country too well and his wife too seldom.

'It was not more than two days since I had last felt the clinging tissues of my blonde Parisienne's vagina draw my semen up through my virile tool when the importunities of the flesh became too strong to be overlooked. I watched Suki glide and sway over the polished inlaid floor while she accompanied herself on the *samisen*.

'Suki knelt down by me and bent her head, tickling my ear with the chrysanthemum in her jet-black hair. "If my poor dancing pleases you," she murmured in Japanese, "perhaps you would deign to let me show you how well I can dance without my feet."

'And she nodded to the screened cubicles leading off from the far end of the room, and her dainty, honey-coloured fingers petted my prick and balls lightly through my trousers. I smiled and took one of her hands in one of mine. She smiled back at me as though to ask what I wished, and I put my other hand to her robe, attempting to pull open the light flowered garment at her breast.

'She was away from me in a flash, her deft fingers disengaging mine expertly and yet without any rebuff implied. I put my hands behind me in a gesture of willingness to refrain from so importunate a type of action.

'Suki smiled and took me by the arm and glided across the room toward the cubicles. I went along with her.

'The apparently blank wall opened at a touch of Suki's fingers, a sliding paper panel exposing a square doorway that led into a small but comfortable cubicle strewn with pillows and lighted by a hanging lantern. There was no bed – the Japanese do not fuck in beds – only a welter of gaily coloured pillows, upon which I threw myself carelessly.

'There was a cherry tree outside the window, heavy with pink and white blossoms, which mingled its cool redolence with the musky perfume of the incense. Suki stood framed in the window for a moment and then came to me.

'She made no objection when now I undid her flowered kimono and exposed her beautiful body. She demurred slightly – the Japanese believe in nudity only for bathing and for religious ceremonies such as the Japanese national dance, but they do not usually fuck naked – however, I overcame her protestations and made her stand before me naked.

'Her body was a miracle of perfection. From her exquisitely coiffed hair with the chrysanthemum set in it to the tips of her embroidered slippers, she was beautiful. Her face olive-shaped and vaguely sad, her throat long and tapering out into perfect little shoulders, from which the long lines of her bosom dropped, supporting two full, globular breasts, generous out of all proportion with her dainty body and a delightfully welcome surprise, therefore, with big plum-like nipples. Her navel was a sudden goblet, and beneath it her belly rounded to become the full mound over her cunt. The hair on it was black and silky, as I was sure of a moment later when I put my arms around her legs and pressed my cheek against the swatch of hair there.

' "Crazy white devil," she whispered affectionately "Do you, too, whimsically desire to be as naked as a mouse?"

'Without waiting for me to assent, she undid my jacket and silk shirt and ran her hands under them on my skin. Her nails were long and pointed, and a thousand little devils of delight surged through me as she scratched my nipples ever so lightly with her nails. I would have hurriedly pulled off my clothes, but that was not Suki's way. She made me sit still while she undid the rest of the buttons and pulled off my jacket. She put her fingers to her coiffure and pulled out a bone pin or two, and her black mop of hair tumbled down in delicious disorder, and she brushed my bare chest with it as she opened my trousers and pushed them down.

'I had on no shoes – they were left at the door of the house when I had entered it – and when my trousers were off, I was naked. Suki could not have her fill of looking at me. She confessed that I was the first white man she had ever seen naked. I was not sure that I believed her, but her extreme delight in touching me seemed to prove the truth of her confession. I found out later that it was entirely true.

'She was particularly taken by my prick, which she found in some respects, it seemed, different from the Japanese variety. At any rate, I doubt if she found it inferior in erectile capacity to the native species, for the wanton and fleeting touches of her fingers, and the warmth of her breath as she bent to examine my prick, all conspired to bring it to quite a respectable degree of stiffness.

'The closeness of her face to my prick suggested to me to put my hands on the back of her head and press her mouth to my tip, and she accepted the suggestion quite willingly. She put out her tongue and tasted away the drop or two of semen that had formed at the tip of my organ with a little chuckle.

'Why she chuckled I cannot say, nor was I in any mood to enquire. I was satisfied to know that she was sucking me off, and well. She took my balls in her agile fingers and squeezed them rhythmically as her mouth flew up and down along my rigid tool. Then, with a plop, her mouth slipped off my prick and she lifted her face and looked enquiringly at me.

' "Ai-nami?" asked she.

'That is the Japanese term for what I call sixty-nine, and the idea was entirely welcome to me, as I had a letch to know how she tasted. I had never sucked a Japanese girl before and I was certain that it would be a pleasant experience. It was. She pressed her mouth back upon my prick and got on her knees and elbows, moving around backward until she could straddle her body over mine and let her twat rest directly over my mouth.

'Then she spread her knees slowly, and as slowly her cunt dropped downward against my mouth, pressing wetly over my half-open lips. I put my arms up around her buttocks and pulled her down tightly to me.

'Her cunt was stickily wet, and its sharp odour assailed my nostrils as I chewed at the soft hot flesh. Her erotic art was perfection itself. She allowed me to set the pace and sucked my cock in the same rhythm in which I licked and munched her cunt, and her fingers dandled my testicles as I squeezed the yielding flesh of her buttocks with one hand and with the other ran a finger into her vagina.

'My whole face was smeared with her juice, my mouth puckered from the tangy flavour, and I sucked and lapped and chewed her cunt in ecstasy. Lingeringly her mouth drew up off my prick and she twisted her head back to me, without, however, letting go of my balls.

' "Do you wish to go on this way," she enquired in an intimate murmur, "or do you wish to fuck me now?"

'I ground my teeth fiercely against her hot and juicy twat once more before I released her. The luscious taste ran like fire through all my body – I could not wait to sink my prick into her very vitals. I pulled my finger out of her vagina, not without a parting jab at her well-developed clitoris, and pushed her up away from me.

'She reversed herself and twisted around on her side, lying with her back to me, her thighs drawn up at right angles to her torso, her legs extended downward at right angles to her thighs. This was the position most common in Japanese screwing – I refer you to the diagrams in Horthy's *Oriental Side-Lying Postures, the Vaginal Axis, and Their Relation to Scientific Screwing* – and I was well-enough acquainted with it to understand what was required of me.

'Suki's cunt peeped out fatly between her thighs as she lay there in that position, the jet black wisps of her hair a dark halo in the dim light of the solitary lantern that lighted the room.

'I rolled over toward her and kneeled in just the way the man kneels in the most usual Occidental position, except that here my thighs were resting against the under surface of both of hers. But the crux of the matter was achieved equally well. My prick fronted brawnily against her twat and, as her officiating hand guided its blind efforts, it sank into her slowly.

'You must understand how different this way of fucking is from most others, for in it lies the particular delight of fucking a Japanese girl. In this method of attaining the age-old but ever new enjoyment, my prick slid into her cunt along the side rather than the bottom of that very juicy passage.

'Where ordinarily a woman heaves up and down in fucking to bring herself and her consort to the desired orgasmic moment, in this position Suki could hardly be expected to do any such thing. The only motion practicable to her was a back-and-forth shaking of her fanny. I rammed forward, letting my weight pass from my knees to my elbows, and my prick sank completely into her vagina while simultaneously she threw her body forward, thus gripping my prick in an oblique and twisting seizure that relaxed as she drew her body back again letting me withdraw for the next stroke.

'I rested on one elbow long enough to push her shoulders down flat so that her upper body was facing up to me, and then I bent further down, pinning her shoulders to the pillows with mine. My face was close to hers and I put my lips forward to kiss her. Her eyes were closed and her facial muscles tense with passion as my doughty plunger dug in and out of her vagina. She could not have been pretending, then, when she reacted in surprise to my kiss and twisted her face to press the side of her nose to mine.

'As you are aware, of course, gentlemen, the kiss is a strictly Occidental practice the Oriental knows it only after being taught – the rubbing of noses together being the analogous Oriental action. Surprised by my kiss, Suki attributed it, perhaps, to bad aim in nose-rubbing. But I was insistent. I slackened my fucking, resting with my prick deep in her juicy tissues, and kissed her full on the mouth again. She reciprocated the kiss this time, hesitantly and awkwardly.

'But her awkwardness only pleased me the more and, silently, I taught her to kiss, rewarding her for every lesson learned by giving her an encouraging stroke with my prick as her lips and tongue responded to the prompting of mine.

'With that sort of bribery for learning, she learned quickly, and our fuck went on with the pleasant adjunct of hot, tongued kisses accompanying it. My body took up the rhythm if had lost momentarily, my prick driving in and out again with my whole weight behind every slow and deliberate stroke into her clinging cunt.

'Suki began her cinder-shifting stroke all over again, jacking higher and higher in my tubes the weighty load of semen that her cunt was aching for. Her hand was still between our thighs, fondling my balls, squeezing them, coaxing them ever so gently.

'My hands held her down, gripping the creamy flesh of her generous teats, and she gloried in the excitement, for her hand pressed over mine, encouraging me to squeeze her yielding boobies while her whole body shook and tossed in the effort to bring both of us to our orgasm. I fucked doggedly, my strokes faster and faster all the time, for I was close to my moment of glory.

'Suki was with me, and as I felt her body heave and quiver with the preliminary ripples of her ecstasy, I realised with that faraway detachment with which all thought is admixed when the orgasm approaches that Suki had told the truth in the silent implications of her many little awkwardnesses that she was but newly a geisha.

'But Suki spent even before I did, moaning and crying out softly – softly, for even at the moment of her crisis, Suki was still a girl of Japan, brought up in houses with walls of paper through which sounds carry with embarrassing clarity. Then, too, she was a delicate creature, and loud, snorting bliss was not for her.

'Her whole body was contorted with pleasure, and her legs shot straight out before her rigidly as I poured my flood of semen into her vagina. I sank forward on her with a sigh, my mouth glued to hers, my prick plunged to the balls in her twat, and I let my juices soak into her clutching tissues, which still gripped and clung as her body quivered and her pulse raced with mine.

'When our bodies finally shook off the delectable lassitude that follows a consummated fuck, Suki pushed me away from her. I was sorry to pull my prick out of so delicious a cunt, and, as I did so, I bent to imprint a grateful kiss on the pouting red lips.

'Then I lay back and stretched pleasurably, only to have Suki roll over on me, her head in my lap. She looked up at me with her dark, shadowy eyes and spoke softly: ' "You kissed my *fooshi* [the Japanese colloquial word for cunt] to say thank you, no?"

'I nodded acquiescence.

' "Then I shall do, too," she continued in Pidgin English, which she spoke with an adorable lisp. And, forthwith, she bent her mouth to my prick and licked off every trace of semen, which she swallowed with no little gusto. She ran her lips down along my prick in order not to miss any, and each time she pulled her lips up over the tip, she pressed a kiss on it. I was becoming stiff again, and so she stopped, placing one last kiss on the slot in the tip of my penis.

' "I shall not stay now," she said, "for if I satisfy you tonight, you may not return tomorrow. Here in Nippon we have a saying that the appetite is kept sharp by rising from the table when still a little hungry. So you will save this and bring it to me tomorrow to hide." She took my prick in her hand as she spoke, and as she finished speaking, gave it a little squeeze.'

~ 13 ~

The Oxford Professor

G. LEGMAN *et al. c.* 1940–50

The popularity of *An Oxford Thesis on Love* (1938) and *The Passionate Pedant* (1939) created an immediate demand for more of the same. Not only did the millionaire who had commissioned the first collection of stories want more, but the population which had been fortunate enough to buy or borrow or rent the mimeoed editions of the books wanted more. There was a clear commercial incentive to continue the series. Lupton Wilkinson, the original author of *An Oxford Thesis*, however, at some point became unwilling or unable to continue the series. With the prospect of money to be made, 'The Organisation' went into action.

'The Organisation' was simply a loosely connected group of booksellers and literary agents in various American cities (especially in New York, Chicago and Los Angeles) with one thing in common, an Ardmore, Oklahoma oil millionaire named Roy Melisander Johnson. Roy Johnson claimed to own and have already read all the erotica that existed in English. Being unable to enjoy a second time any book he had previously read, he decided to commission new erotica for his private reading pleasure. He contacted the same people who in past years had supplied him with printed pornography, mainly booksellers in large cities, and requested that they supply him with two new erotic books a week. As he was willing to pay $200 for each hundred-page manuscript (more for anything from Henry Miller) they were happy to oblige, even though Johnson directed that half of the money should go to the authors. Many of these booksellers were also publishers on the side, and because of the Depression, it was not hard for them to find out-of-work or struggling writers who were willing to churn out one-hundred-page erotic typescripts for $1.00 a page, or else to locate literary agents with clients willing to join in this project. Money was short all over. The first authors recruited friends, and the ranks of those in the anonymous employ of the millionaire swelled. And so a new American cottage industry began.

The workings of 'The Organisation', while originally highly secret and clandestine, have recently been documented in various books published by former members of this erotica Cartel. One need only read Anaïs Nin's *Diaries* (volume three especially), Bernie Wolfe's *Memoirs of a Not Altogether Shy Pornographer*, Milton Luboviski's affidavit published in 'Henry Miller's' *Opus Pistorum*, or any of several Gershon Legman opuses, including his *Horn Book* and the introduction to Kearney's *Private Case*. The authors for the most part worked alone, at home, at their typewriters. They turned in their finished manuscripts to the local agent, who frequently paid them less than the agreed-upon $1.00 a page. Many found it increasingly difficult, if not totally boring, to produce pornography on a scheduled basis. To alleviate the tedium several of the authors in the New York group started to gather together.

Anaïs Nin gives a wonderful description of how she and her friends (male and female) would jointly write erotic literature round-robin (a technique employed thirty years later to produce the bestselling *Naked Came the Stranger* by 'Penelope Ashe'), only to be told by the millionaire that he wanted less literary art and more lust! Nin relates how the male homosexuals in her group wrote erotica as if they were women, while the 'wallflowers' wrote about orgies, and the most sensitive and chaste of the group (after reading Krafft-Ebing's *Psychopathia Sexualis*) wrote of the most bestial perversions. Bernie Wolfe tells how he got kicked out of the enterprise for demanding more money, and then made a deal with Henry Miller, who at this time was no longer interested in writing pornography for the millionaire. They agreed that Wolfe would continue to write pornography which Miller would then turn in as his own, with the two splitting the extra $1-2 a page that the millionaire paid for erotica from 'Henry Miller'. (In an extremely technical sense Johnson got what he paid extra for, as these manuscripts did literally come to the New York agent from Henry Miller.)

The fraternity of writers anonymously commissioned by Johnson was impressive. In addition to the above named, there were also Robert Sewall (the brilliant pastiche author of *The Devil's Advocate*), Clement Wood (author, poet, editor and *bon vivant*), Robert De Niro Sr (poet and father of the famous actor), Robert Bragg (aka 'Bob De Mexico'), Caresse Crosby (widow of the famous American expatriate publisher of

Paris's Black Sun Press), Jack Hanley, Gene Fowler, Anton Gud, George Barker (the English poet), Virginia Admiral (the painter), Harvey Breit, Robert Duncan, Clifton Cuthbertson, Paul Little (the most prolific American author of erotica with over four hundred novels to his credit) and many more whose names and deeds have over the years slid into literary obscurity.

Gershon Legman has written of how he gave over his part of the *Oxford Professor* enterprise to his friend Robert Sewall as he found that writing pornography made him impotent! Hence the Oxford Professor series became a collection of related short erotic stories written by various authors over the period *c.*1937–50, with the New York branch of 'The Organisation' providing the sequels to *An Oxford Thesis of Love*. Legman, Sewall and others each contributed chapters. The ribbon copies of the text were sent to the millionaire, while the middlemen kept carbon copies that they ordered from the authors and typists. Every so often, as the demand developed, several of the stories would be published together by these enterprising middlemen for their own additional profit, all unbeknownst to Johnson. The first of these collections, as we have seen, was *An Oxford Thesis on Love* (1938), which was followed the next year by *The Passionate Pedant*. Both of these were crudely printed in mimeo form with erotic illustrations by Emile Ganzo. Other collections of these stories subsequently appeared, typeset, over the years under such titles as *Torrid Tales*, *South of the Border*, *The Professor's Tale* and *The Oxford Professor*. This last title seems to have been published *c.*1950, and its 239 pages consist of six stories, entitled 'The Choir Loft', 'Alpine Annie', 'Tenacious Theresa', 'Dipsomaniacal Daisy', 'Jacinthe' and 'Leslie'. Octavo in size, it was poorly printed by offset, illustrated with copies of previously published erotic art and photographs, and badly perfect bound. Yet it still retained the wit and flavour of the very first collection of Oxford Professor tales, as it proclaimed itself: '*The Oxford Professor*. In which L. Erectus Mentulus, PH.D., late of Oxford College, is taken further in the narration of his adventures and misadventures, erotic, alcoholic, and otherwise; not to mention a choice accompaniment of drolleries, notes and *excursi* of one sort or another, metaphysical & also miscellaneously edifying and entertaining. *Ad cordem feminae via – per vulva sua est*. Done By The Hand Of The Author Into A Manuscript At Natchitoches, Louisiana.'

Here then is one final lecture . . .

from *The Oxford Professor*

'Hank here was just telling us a story,' the salesman explained to the professor. 'It seems that – but you tell it, Hank. It's funny as hell.'

'It really isn't so funny,' he said deprecatingly; 'It was just about a time I was swimming with a girl and tried to fuck her in the water. It was up near Boston, in the ocean, you see, and – oh, it just didn't work. We'd lay on the sand and she'd play around until I had a good hard-on, and then we'd run into the water and try to get to work. But by the time we got out far enough, I wouldn't have anything to work with any more. Then we tried floating and sucking each other. But that didn't work either. Everything tasted of salt, and we half drowned in the bargain.'

'I should venture to say,' began the professor, 'that, on the whole, such experiments generally prove entirely unsatisfactory.' Then he subsided as he saw Dave returning with three bottles tucked carefully under his arm. 'Ah,' exclaimed the professor as the proprietor of the soft-drink parlour, wiping the imaginary dust of antiquity from the bottles on to an already filthy apron, set the graceful containers on the table. 'And whose was the happy suggestion that we should test the Montrachet?'

The druggist acknowledged the honour.

'Well, why can't you fuck in the water?' asked the barber, ever eager for knowledge of the carnal variety.

'An aquatic fucking is not only possible; it is delightful, once the obvious natural obstacles have been removed,' the professor said. 'In fact, one of the most unusual experiences of my life centred around such an incident.'

'Now wait a minute,' interposed the druggist, a trifle ruffled. 'I spent almost a whole afternoon trying to figure that thing out, and – and – well, I just don't think it can be done!'

'And thus,' sighed the professor, 'have the achievements of all great leaders been maligned. However, to set your mind at rest, I will admit at once that the conditions under which you laboured were such that you incurred no disgrace in defeat. My own experience was attended by the most painstaking preparation, an effete artificiality, in fact. It happened in Paris many years ago, and the girl, although I am certain that such was not her name, was known to me simply as Jacinthe.

'I was studying under Henri Robespierre Touques Le Poittevain, the man whose later *Fundamental Facts about Farting (Faits Fondamentals sur Petant)* was such a bad-smelling scandal at the time of its publication, and I was living with two other young students who were busy inventing a language which they hoped to teach at the expense of the government.

'Richard, who is now a streetcar conductor in Des Moines, was a quiet, retiring fellow who was bent on educating himself. Bill, however, was more socially inclined. His nose was more frequently in a cunt than in a book, and by pushing himself forward at every opportunity, he had been accepted into the best circles of Paris.

'Bill was one of the coolest men I have ever known. He was as immovable as an old Turk; the lightning might have come down to light his pipe and he would have shown not the least astonishment. So, therefore, when he burst into our rooms one night and roared that he had just met the most amazing woman in the whole of France, I was quite ready to believe him.

By the time he managed to break into his glowing description of this marvellous creature long enough to tell me that we were invited to call on her, his contagious enthusiasm had affected me, and when he finally got around to revealing that the appointment was for that very evening, I began to dress without further delay. And at some time around nine, we presented ourselves at the door of an address in one of the less presentable quarters of the city. All was tumult, smoke and rain, ugliness and misery, a smell of sewage and gasoline under a grey sky. It was a hideous, ignoble section, hardly appropriate to the most amazing woman in France.

'Then, as the door was opened to our insistent ringing, we were suddenly plunged into the direct antithesis of all this.

'I cannot describe the place. It seemed that the whole universe must have been ransacked, that each country had given up its utmost luxury to the end that, in the midst of the squalor and filth of that mean setting, a hidden fairyland of crowning magnificence could be created.

'Yatumani Norashashu Hirosata, in a lecture before the Catalonian Society for the Classification, Glorification and Continuation of Cunt, stated that the ear can be trained to detect, even in the faintest whisper, the exact pitch to which a woman's passions are aroused, and that it can be determined to just what degree she is latently passionate.

It may well be that Yatumani was right, and that, like fingerprints, there are certain vocal characteristics that cannot be disguised. It is possible that we may yet see the happy day when, on first hearing a young lady's voice, we will be able to determine whether or not she will be willing to suck our cock that evening.

'At any rate, a few words of perfect French, coming from behind me, sent a delicious electric prickling up my spine and ruffing the hairs on the back of my neck. It was a perfect example of one of the variant secondary sexual manifestations as noted by Bruno Victor Schweiteringshaften von Wenckebacker in his *Klapusterbeeren und Ihren Sexualwissenschaftlicher Vermehrlichkeit.*

'I turned, and there was Jacinthe. She was one of the race of Javanese, those graceful vampires who drain the balls and purse of an Occidental in three weeks, leaving him as dry as a squeezed lemon, and she could not have been more than eighteen. Her brows were of deep, velvety black, melting to bluish tints at her temples. And by some charming oddity, her eyes were blue. As to the colour of her skin, some transparencies of the amber may give you an idea.

' "Rima and I have been expecting you," she said, and for the first time I noticed that she was accompanied by another girl of her own race – lovely, but of a beauty that was lost in contrast to that of Jacinthe. She crossed the room and took my arm, and the girl named Rima took possession of Bill.

'I will not bore you with details of the early part of the evening. We had dinner and we talked. And then, as the last course was served, Rima stood up and touched Bill on the shoulder. They excused themselves and he followed her out of the room.

' "You are, of course, free to spend the night?" Jacinthe asked.

' "Good," Jacinthe replied as I assured her that my time was open. "Then let's not waste any of it." And she led me out of a doorway opposite to that through which Bill and Rima had disappeared, and we entered her bedroom. She pointed to a richly brocaded dressing gown that was laid out on her bed. Then she disappeared for a few minutes.

'I had hardly time to change into the robe and step into a pair of woolly bedroom slippers when the girl was back clad in a diaphanous, tailored négligé. It clung to her more like a cloud than a garment, and its presence served only to shadow, not conceal, her pert charm.

'Her legs were slim almost to childishness, crowned at their juncture by a blue-black triangle of curls, in the centre of which I could discern but the slightest hint of a tight, pink slit. Her teats were small, mounted with nipples so flaming that I knew they must be stained, and her belly was youthfully flat. Altogether she was so temptingly fuckable that my prick leaped at the sight of her and an unconcealable bulge began to poke out the front of the robe I was wearing.

'Jacinthe stepped across the room with the easy indolence of a cat and slipped into my arms, rubbing her belly against the bulky evidence of my prick and making low, purring noises in her throat. Her hand moved down over the robe, and her fingers tightened around my tool, testing its thickness and strength. I slid one of my hands to her bottom and began to stroke the warm flesh of her ass through the spider-web silk of her négligé, while the other fingered open the front of the garment and burrowed in to touch her boobies. They jiggled under my palm, and the ruby nipples rose and stiffened until they stood out like grapes.

'Jacinthe's fingers went between the folds of the brocaded gown and touched warmly against my balls. She plucked at the hairs that sprinkled them until they were set swaying, then caught them in her cupping palm and shook them playfully. She tickled in between my thighs, running her light fingertips back over the ridge that was tightening stiffly as my rod grew more and more rampant. When they were almost at my asshole, her dancing fingers reversed and ran back again to my cock. She stroked up the length to the very tip, wrapped her fingers lightly around my prick at the base and slid them slowly to the tip, releasing it there and returning her hand to the base again with a subtle milking motion.

'I was playing with her nipples, tweaking and pinching them as they grew harder and harder, longing to set my mouth to them, but reluctant to make any move that might disturb her slipping fingers from their game. Her boobies yielded softly as I squeezed them, and her little cunt seemed to quiver under my stroking.

'Jacinthe's tiny hand clutched tighter and tighter at my prick, and I could fairly feel the colourless oil being squeezed through the hot tube and out the deep slot at the tip. Then she slowly pushed back the loose foreskin so that the knobby end was bared, and her thumb moved softly on the sensitive surface, spreading the oily juice over it and down along the whole length of my prick. I looked longingly toward the bed, and Jacinthe caught my glance.

' "Later," she said, suddenly slipping away and disentangling my reluctant arms. Then she led me, with an air of dark mystery, through a door concealed by a Persian hanging and into a magnificent bathroom.

'Pale green paintings, representing mythological subjects – such as Diana and Callisto, Leda surprised by the swan, Salamacis and

Hermaphrodite – occupied carved frames of reed on the walls. Small blue and white porcelain squares covered the floor to the very edge of a huge, sunken tub which was even now filled with steaming water. Hidden lights cast a subdued green tint over everything and glinted on the still water of the bath.

'Jacinthe dropped her négligé on to a couch by the door, stepped out of her slippers, and tiptoed to the edge of the little pool. Little ripples stirred the surface as she touched one tiny foot to the water.

'It was evidently too warm, for she touched a faucet button briefly before calling me to her side. And as I dropped the gown I was wearing and went to the edge of the tub, I saw that it was far more deep than I had imagined, being, as I shortly discovered, of a depth such that the water came almost to my shoulders and completely covered Jacinthe's.

'There was a little ladder at one end of the pool, but the girl disregarded it. By merely stepping off the edge, she suddenly plunged in, showering me with her splashing.

'She looked up laughingly, stretched out her legs and floated lazily beneath me. Sparkling drops of water clung to her little belly like a net of pearls, and the water rolled over her in transparent waves. I watched for only a minute, and then sprang in after her.

'The temperature of the water was higher than I had expected, and for a moment I felt some discomfort. Then, as my body adjusted itself, the discomfort passed and every muscle in my body seemed to be relaxing. I allowed my feet to leave the bottom of the tub and floated alongside Jacinthe for a minute. Then I reached to her, but she kicked her little feet quickly and, amidst a furious splashing, drifted out of my reach with the slow grace of an ocean liner.

'But she could not go far for the tub – or perhaps I should say pool – was no more than twelve feet in either dimension, and I was immediately after her. I caught her in my arms, submerging us both for the moment, and when, with a great sputtering and gasping, we returned to the surface, I pulled her body close to me.

'Standing now, I lifted her body, which, buoyed by the water, was light as her gossamer négligé, until her dripping teats were on a level with my face. Then I thrust my head forward, caressing the luscious hemispheres with my cheeks. I pushed my nose between them, and, as I did so, Jacinthe caught them suddenly together, playfully imprisoning my nose. Her nipples were crushed against my cheeks, and when I shook my head to wanton in her breasts, they grew taut and firm once more.

'My hands were clutched strongly into the soft flesh of the girl's young buttocks, and her wet pelt was pressed close to my belly. She spread her legs far apart, and beneath the surface of the green water they shimmered, white and oddly foreshortened. I looked down at her black muff, watching the little hairs weaving like searching tentacles, back and forth with the eddying motion of the water, and I noticed also that the shock of the hot water, coupled with the violent motions of our bodies, had served – if I may strain the figure – to reduce my so boldly presented axiom to an absurdity.

'Jacinthe noticed it also, and at the same time that I let her down and sent one palm swimming to her twat like a small flounder, she reached for my deflated organ. Her fingers wrapped around the limp tool, which at the moment reminded me of nothing so much as some pink, blind sea worm, and she pressed back the skin to make the analogy complete by giving the flaccid creature a head. As the shrunken tip was forced out, it was momentarily set a tingle as the hot water stung it, and a thousand prickles ran back to my balls and thence up my spine. But this passed and, as the girl in natural continuity began to masturbate me, I was pleased to note that my prick began to raise itself to quite respectable proportions.

'I had by this time managed to slip one finger between her thighs and along the closed mouth of her twat. The fuzz-covered outer lips were pressed firmly together, giving some hint of the tightness that was to be found behind them, and when I twisted my finger between them, they pinched it almost reproachfully.

'Within, the soft inner lips were slippery with the girl's love juice. The soft parts moved easily enough as I slid my finger back and forth, and the clitoris bunched tightly as I pressed it. Suddenly I felt a hungry desire to kiss the pretty cunt, and I ducked my head beneath the water to do just that.

'The attempt was not wholly unsuccessful, but neither was it satisfactory, and Jacinthe, when she saw what it was that I wanted, presented the solution. Arching her back and throwing back her head, she allowed herself to float once more.

'I saw at once the possibility presented by her. By slipping between her legs so that their weight rested partly on me, and then supporting the rest of her body by a slight upward pressure of my palms in the small of her back, I was able to lift her hips far enough out of the water that I could suck without strangling and give more pleasure to her also.

'My mouth clamped over the wet pelt and I pressed the water out of it with my tongue. But as fast as I squeezed it dry, another little wave would wash over it, so I gave up this pleasure in order to slip my tongue into her pink slit. My head dipped farther and I licked over the puffed outer lips, where lingered only the vaguest hint of her sweet cunt taste.

'The soaked hairs between her thighs tickled against my lips as I pressed my mouth close to her twat, and when my tongue slipped into the pink crack and picked its way back over the oily surfaces to the upstart clitoris, I felt the girl's hips twitch buoyantly. Her body swayed rhythmically, rising and falling on the tides our motions set in action, and as each movement rubbed her cunt and the inner sides of her thighs tightly to my face, she must soon have felt a more urgent desire rising within her even had my tongue not been seeking warmly into her twat and curling into its intimate folds.

'She started to roll her hips from side to side, freely and without effort, and she clutched my supporting arms to crush her cunt more firmly to my face. The soft parts were mashed on my mouth, and the sweet, musk juice was forced from them like wine from grapes in the press, like wine, too, it was not only a delight to the palate, but spun quickly to my brain, warmed my heart and set my pulse pounding and my loins throbbing.

'I licked and sucked zestfully, curling my tongue upward and back into the tight opening of her vagina. I ran it in and out with the imperative movements of fucking, and beneath my fingers the tender, mounded buttocks of the girl tightened and quivered as her hips moved in reciprocal action. Her twat clasped my tongue as it might have clasped a prick, and the tangy taste of it filtered completely through my mouth, delighting my senses.

' "Now let me suck you," Jacinthe said, suddenly freeing herself and balancing lightly on her toes. "I want your cock to be really big when you fuck me, *mignon*."

'In general it may be said that the male body does not float so easily as the female, due to the fatty padding that covers the latter and lends it that soft curvaciousness upon which we so dote. The average woman may, therefore, even in time of shipwreck or flood, have a life expectancy somewhat greater than that of her leaner Adam. Still, I found it not at all difficult to couch my weight while Jacinthe satisfied her hunger to taste my prick. I locked my hands behind my head and stared blissfully up at the ceiling while the girl set to work.

'First Jacinthe pressed her shoulders under my upper thighs and raised my hips somewhat. Then she wound her arms around my body from beneath and took my prick in both hands, pulling it to her so that the angle of declivity was less sharp. Her deft fingers set to masturbating me, and my prick was soon as sturdily erect as ever I have seen it. The whole rigid length, when she squeezed the base, swelled ferociously, and the network of bluish veins stood out sharply from the ruddy surface.

'Jacinthe's strange blue eyes lighted with deep, glowing fires as she stared at the red tip, and her lips parted slightly. She licked her tongue over her lips and slowly bent her head to my crotch. Her red tongue searched out, touched the tip of my prick, and licked thrillingly over the swollen glans as one free hand sought my bollocks. Then she touched her tongue tip into the ridge at the back of the knob and licked around it. Her full lips touched the moulded end, and closed over it. She pushed forward and took my prick wholly into her mouth.

'Now, as she began to suck me, her lips moved up and down over my tool. She twisted her head a little with each motion, moving the slipping skin around in corkscrew fashion, and her palm, though I could not see it, was curled under my balls, joggling them up and down under the water. Her teeth pinched at the base of my prick when she had gulped in as much of that burly organ as she well could without choking, and as she slid her mouth back to the tip, their pressure was not wholly released until they caught on the knob itself, when, after nibbling the rubbery thing for a moment, she would then thrust forward to repeat the performance. Or she would let my prick drop almost free from her mouth, suck it in with a sudden gulp, and then, lips closed firmly over its first inch or so, shake her head with a startling ferocity that sent drops of water splashing to the walls and deep thrills of passion surging through my whole body. And during all this by-play, she continuously sucked my tool as though her life depended on bringing me to an orgasm. And I should shortly have arrived and spent in her mouth – for I was riding quite comfortably in the arms of our miniature Pacific and saw no need to change – had not she seen how far her ministering was leading me. Then, just as my prick began those strange twitchings that foretell an orgasm, she suddenly ceased her impassioned mouthings and paddled over to one side of the bath, where, reaching into a drawer like compartment, she produced a small jade jar. Dipping her fingers into this, she took on her palm a small amount of a colourless substance that she evidently kept for just such a purpose. Returning to me, she began to rub it briskly over my prick. In no time at all, my rigid member was completely waterproofed and thoroughly lubricated. This accomplished, she wiped the remainder from her hands with a soft linen towel.

'I saw immediately why she had done this. In fact, I had been conjecturing for some time as to just how successful a complete fucking could be, for the water was certain to wash away any natural lubricants as soon as they were manufactured. And, following her next move, I learned how the mechanics of the thing were to be accomplished.

'A bar, somewhat like an ordinary metal rack for towels, was set into the side of the little pool at a height some few inches above the water's surface. Jacinthe now grasped this and twisted on to her back, spreading her legs for me to come between, and arching her back desirously. I moved to her and, grasping the bar also, pulled my body part way over hers. Thus, half submerged, we were in the usual face-to-face position for screwing.

'Due to the resistance of the water, all of our motions were retarded to a pace much slower than that normal to such matters – a tempo, in fact, much reminiscent of that produced in motion pictures by the use of the erroneously termed slow camera. And as I pressed the tip of my prick against the waiting lips of her twat, I could not but mark how akin to the unreal actions of a dream were my movements now.

'The head of my cock burrowed smoothly between the puffed cunt lips, and as I rolled my hips from side to side to set it well in, I set up a gentle backwash that raised and lowered both our bodies alternately and was not to cease until our fucking was quite finished. The hairy mouth, accepting the knob of my prick quite greedily, closed over it and seemed to be mouthing for more. I felt Jacinthe's twat begin to twitch inwardly, and as I gently pushed another inch or so of my tool back over the inner lips, over the erect clitoris and up to her vagina, the twitching no longer confined itself solely to her cunt, but began to transmit itself to the soft butts of her ass. Her bottom was set aquiver as I forced my burly prick home, and she wrapped her legs about me to pull me closer.

'I thrust forward carefully, for Jacinthe's cunt was so tight that I was afraid my tool might cause her pain. But I need have had no fear. The girl wriggled her hips delightedly as more and more of the stiff tool disappeared into her, and she forced herself to take it faster. Still, I frigged cautiously until almost the whole stiff length was in her; then, confident that she could take it all with ease, I jammed the remaining few inches in with as forceful a thrust as I could manage.

'Jacinthe laughed happily as the hot knob pressed into the clasping channels of her vagina, and she rolled her bottom to make the contact even more pronounced. The oiled skin of my prick slipped easily over the tender tissues of her twat as it rubbed about within her, and I was so far into her that the eager lips of her cunt were mouthing my pelt.

'Supporting myself now with one hand, I grasped her shaking buttocks and squeezed them fiercely as I fucked her. The yielding flesh rolled softly beneath my grasp. Jacinthe wanted more and more of my prick in her. She moved her hips continually in a querulous, searching manner and tried to slide down on the rod and impale herself. So I began to give her still more of my tool, slowly, an inch at a time.

'The walls of her cunt closed tightly around my prick as it slid into the girl, the tight mouth clasping and unclasping in a series of hungry twitchings. Her hips were rocking back and forth in time to my fucking, and she twisted vigorously in impatient attempts to take in one thrust more of my tool than was advisable. Very shortly practically all of it was buried and she was thrashing about so aimlessly, so searchingly, that I knew she must be nearing her climax.

'And I was quite ready to spend with her. My balls were drawn tightly up, and the desires of my whole body, centred in my cock, were at a high pitch. The delightful pinching and squeezing my prick was receiving from the contractions of Jacinthe's cunt were sending messages of the utmost imperativeness scurrying through me, and I hovered time after time on the very brink of the chasm that would drop me into a whirling, down-rushing thrill.

'Quickly,' I breathed hoarsely. 'I want to give my sperm to your belly – now!'

'Jacinthe rolled rapidly and I began ramming my prick into her with complete abandon. As the bursting tool pistoned back and forth in her vagina, it sloshed strongly in the water it had forced into her from the tub. A string of little bubbles sprang from her cunt and jiggled bouncily to the surface.

'Jacinthe wound her legs about me once more and we kept fucking fiercely. My cock was in her to the balls at each thrust, and if it had been possible, I believe we would have put them in as well. I put my mouth to one of the girl's red nipples and sucked at it until it seemed that it must come off. And then we spent.

'A hot, searing flood of molten silver poured from my bollocks as they plunged and shook. My body was arched forward with the paradoxical effort of ridding itself as quickly as possible of the burden whose losing was so delicious, and my cock strained and swelled in Jacinthe's vagina as the precious stream was cast through it. Jet after burning jet was spilled into her twat, which was convulsed with the paroxysm of her own orgasm.

'Our legs and arms, our entire bodies arched as we drained the reservoirs of pleasure to the last drop. Jacinthe stared at me with the mute eyes of a gazelle that has just received a spear in its heart, while I set my teeth so sharply into her shoulder that I tasted the salty sting of blood on my tongue. And then it was over and gone.

'We released each other and floated side by side in the bath until the water was quite calm again, and only the faintest of ripples caressed our bodies. At last we turned to the ladder and climbed out dripping, on to the porcelain-tiled floor.

'Pinkly naked and gleaming with wetness, Jacinthe handed me a large, soft towel. Taking another for herself, she began to pat herself dry, but I took it from her, wiped her tiny feet and rubbed her briskly until her skin glowed with a deep, inner lustre. Then, when we were completely dry, we went back to the bedroom.

'The bed was wide, made for sport more than for sleeping, and Jacinthe climbed into it merrily, rolling about like a playful bear cub. I caught her in my arms and tussled with her briefly. Then my hands were once more at her twat.

'Would you like to suck me some more?' she asked, as my fingers played with her puffed cunt lips.

'The question had hardly time to leave her pretty mouth before I was curled at her knees, pushing my nose into the still damp curls of her pelt and pressing a hot, sucking kiss to the pink slot itself. Her own fingers moved down to spread the outer lips for me, and the honey-scented twat opened before my eyes like a pale flower.

'My tongue slid out and moved over the dainty parts slowly, hunting out every secret fold, every honey-laden crevice. And now I caught the full flavour of her juicy cunt.

'Her clitoris was soft at first, but as I continued to mouth her, as I plucked at the puffed lips, fuller than those that nipped them, and as I nibbled tenderly at the folding inner ones, the little organ stiffened to button-like hardness. I pressed it with my tongue, and it sprang back resiliently. Her love liquor flowed more and more freely, until my cheeks were bathed in it and my mouth was filled with its spicy taste.

' "I will come this way," she said. "But I want you to come, too." And with that, she bent down so that her face was in my own crotch.

'This time she sucked my prick into her mouth with a single gesture. It was tumescent, but not rigid, as she moved to take it, and so she was able to take quite all of it at first, and she sucked it with an avidity that was not only pleasant to watch but soon gave evidence that my cock would shortly be as eagerly throbbing as ever before.

'There were a thousand and one things I wanted to know about Jacinthe, as she called herself, but whatever questions I had intended to put to this unusual person were forgotten, or at least put out of mind, as I went back to licking and sucking her cunt. For there was forgetfulness between that lovely girl's thighs. With my nose pressed to her dripping twat, my nostrils savouring her deep scent and my lips glued to the palpitating grotto from which flowed her delicious love liquor, I could have forgotten everything. Seldom have I been so lost in cunt as I was with Jacinthe and yet, not too far lost to sense and appreciate what she offered.

'My prick grew stiffer and thicker until it was soon more than a mouthful for her. Lips stretched over the burly rod, she slid her face back and forth at my crotch, thrusting the heavy prick far back into her throat. Her mouth and my cock were wet and glistening with saliva, and she sucked it juicily as though to draw the sperm from my balls by sheer dragging force.

'Jacinthe's fingers tangled in my hair and she played briefly with the lobe of my ear. She locked her legs about my neck and held me crushingly close to her lovely cunt. Her bottom shook wildly and she ground her hips so fiercely to my face that her springy pelt scratched my cheeks.

' "Dai-erima," she murmured in her native tongue, and even though I did not at that time know the language, her meaning was clear.

'I pulled my prick away from her so that she could give her whole attention over to the upswelling surge of her orgasm, and I licked and drank at her twat with ever-increasing intensity. Then, with a sudden flaming rush like that with which the sun bursts over the hills of her native land, the girl was flung into a paroxysm of wild, delirious passion.

'I was almost smothered, so closely did she crush me to her, and her strong legs tightened around my neck until I thought it must snap. She thrashed about violently, crawling over the coverlet of the bed like a wounded animal, dragging my body with her as a puma drags a trap. She cried out piercingly – once.

'When her climax had passed, I made no attempt to approach her. I lay alongside her spent body as she lay, eyes closed as if in sleep, until she should be ready to come to me. Then, as her eyes fluttered languorously open again, my patience was rewarded in the gratitude that shone out of them.

'She crept down to take my prick in her mouth once more, and now that her own pleasure was – at least, for the moment – spent, she hastened to bring me also to that final delight which was recently hers. Her tongue curled searingly over my rod, licked down to my balls and back up the sturdy barrel to the oozing tip. She licked wetly over the ridge.

'I could no longer hold off my spending now, and just as she thrust her lips far down toward the thick base, I came in her lovely mouth.

She swallowed mouthful after mouthful and still milked my prick avidly for the last drops. Then she crept up into my arms and we fell asleep.'

'That was some story,' the barber said enthusiastically as the professor tapped the straw-tipped end of a cigarette on his fingernail and prepared to light it. 'But tell me, professor, did you look real close at her cunt? I mean, maybe it was just the least little bit – sideways?'

'Joe can't give up that idea that somewhere in this world there are women with oblique cunts,' the druggist laughed. 'I hear he's even been bothering the librarian to get him books about it.'

'You know, Joe,' the salesman said seriously, 'the Eskimo women have their cunts under their left armpits.'

~ 14 ~

White Stains

Anaïs Nin *and Friends c.*1940

About the year 1940 there appeared one of the strangest volumes of *sub rosa* erotic literature ever to appear in this century. What set it so apart from the vast majority of that day's erotica was that its fiction was extremely sensual, almost poetically so, and was more skilfully written than most of the literature of any genre of the time. The book also had a pronounced air of mystery. Literally every piece of information on its title page, *including its title*, was false or misleading!

The book in question was entitled: '*White Stains* by Ernest Dowson . . . Privately Published by Isidor Liseux. Paris'. The deceit was instantly obvious. The book first appeared in New York City at a time when Liseux was already nearly fifty years dead. The called for 'Five Illustrations by Aubrey Beardsley In His Most Erotic Vein' were simply not present. Those in the literary know immediately recognised the writing to be not at all in the manner of the famous *fin-de-siècle* English poet and translator Ernest Dowson, perhaps best know in the United States for his works published by the London-based Leonard Smithers, and for his work with Aubrey Beardsley's circle on such projects as the Smithers-published *Yellow Book* and *Savoy* magazines. Perhaps, some conjectured, the author could be a different person of the same name?

Even the title rang false. There already existed an infamous, obscene, and sacrilegious tome entitled *White Stains*. It was no secret that the book (anonymously published by Leonard Smithers!) was the work of the mystic occultist Aleister Crowley, and that that book had been banned, seized and destroyed all over the world. Crowley's volume, while erotic in vein, for the most part disgusted those who read it.

The *White Stains* that appeared *c.*1940 was nothing like this. It was a somewhat schizophrenic production, for it contained an explicit sex manual, 'The Contemporary [and most exhaustive] Love's Cyclopaedia', plus six erotic short stories, novellas actually, each complete in itself. Where the 'Cyclopaedia' was probably a rewriting of the nineteenth-century classic *The Horn Book*, presented in modern, direct, blunt, to-the-sexual-point language, replete with socially unacceptable sexual slang, it was the fiction pieces that drew the attention and astonishment. They were simple and lyrical expressions of complex erotic and sexual feelings. Sensuality rather than sexuality *per se* was the predominant theme, although the two were juxtaposed and finely tuned to each other. Even when graphic and sexually explicit, it was hard to classify the tales as obscene or pornographic. They were simply too beautifully written.

Over the years this *White Stains* has yielded some of its secrets. The man responsible for it has been identified as Samuel Roth, the New York City poet, author, bookseller, magazine editor, publisher, mail-order pioneer, and all around *litterateur*. (The printed book was even bound in Roth's signature, red endpapers, as if as a clue to the public.) According to Gershon Legman, the dean of living erotobibliophiles and folklorists, Roth so liked the sound of the Crowley book's title he decided to reprint it sight unseen. However, when he actually read the book, he found it too vitriolic and scurrilous. Roth then opted to drop the Crowley text but keep the title for his own use! He simply appended it to a more agreeable erotic text. The attribution of this new book to Dowson may have been a Roth marketing ploy, to attract the commercial attention of his literary mail-order-book customers who were interested in the poet Dowson's crafted verse and prose; the title alone had already attracted the attention of those eager to obtain the tabooed and forbidden Crowley item.

Who then wrote the six delicious novellas? That is no mean detective job. In form, style, and content they are very reminiscent of the Depression-period-commissioned ('dollar a page') erotica produced by Anaïs Nin and her literary friends in New York. These *White Stains* short stories compare favourably with those acknowledged Nin pieces published openly for the first time in the late 1970s in collections entitled *Delta of Venus* and *Little Birds*. In fact the pieces in *White Stains* bring to mind a complaint Nin noted in her diary for December 1940, writing that the anonymous patron commissioning this new erotica was unhappy because the pieces she and her friends were penning had too much poetry! The patron was later identified as the Oklahoma oil millionaire Roy M. Johnson, who directed that he wanted stories that were narrative, direct, specific, concentrated on sex and without philosophy or analysis. Obviously Johnson did not appreciate that the mind, and not the groin, is the most erogenous part of the human body.

The actual authorship of the delicate fiction in *White Stains* will probably forever remain speculation only. In theory, one could imagine Roth intercepting copies or carbons of typescripts meant for the Oklahoman, or commissioning some on his own (although that was not his style), and surreptitiously printing them *sub-rosa* for his own financial gain.

Over the years this volume has become forgotten. No one has openly claimed it for their own, and only those fortunate enough to have found a copy of the increasingly rare original volume have had the opportunity to savour its pleasures and artistry.

~~~ from *White Stains*

Alice I used to meet her at dances during the winter. She was a wonderful dancer and a little beauty. Needless to say, holding her in my arms in dancing made me wish to know her better. It was not long before little pressures of hands and arms were asking, and answering, unspoken questions. Without a word said, she let me know that someday she would consent to more.

Later, in the spring, we used to go walking together in the hills on pleasant afternoons. We would drive out into the country, hide the car somewhere on a quiet road, and wander off into fresh green woods. We were fond of a most secluded little glade which we found one day, where we often rested, sure of being undisturbed. But Alice, though generous with kisses and dear little caresses, entirely withheld herself otherwise, and I was entirely too fond of her – and too interested in discovering under what circumstances she would give herself – to press matters beyond showing her clearly what I wanted. She quite understood all the time, and I knew it was only a question of time until she would be brought to the point of giving me all that I asked.

Her surrender came under the unusual circumstances which I am about to describe. One lovely, warm afternoon in May, we found our way to our little glade, but were very much surprised to find two other young lovers there before us. Totally engaged in each other, they did not hear us, and we stealthily withdrew a little distance and sat down in a little pocket among the bushes to see what would happen. Alice, I could easily see, was very much excited and interested.

The girl was lying on her back in the shade of a tree. The man lay beside her, and their lips were together. We could hear the indistinct murmur of their voices. Hunched up as we two were in our little hiding place, quite close together, I did not find it hard, nor think it wrong, to put my lips to Alice's. Alice clearly thought my conduct fitting, for she returned my kiss, with interest. The interest was paid in a tiny flutter of her tongue-tip against my lips. Our kiss lasted quite a time.

When we looked again, the scene had changed somewhat. Alice gasped a little, and well she might. The lover was lying on one side, propped up on an elbow, and his free hand was disturbing the formerly smooth folds of his sweetheart's skirt. Perhaps to keep her attention from what his hand was doing – at any rate, to keep her attention divided – he was kissing her quite ardently. But his hand was under her skirt and had pulled it up so that we could see two shapely legs in pale blue stockings. Two small feet in pale blue slippers (very unsuitable for walking in the hills) were calmly crossed. The lover was caressing the pale blue stockings.

'Peter,' whispered Alice, remonstrating. For as she crouched, somewhat curled up, one very attractive leg, as far as the knee, lay outside of the shelter of her skirt, and my hand rested on the dark green silk that covered it. But her attention must have been distracted, for after that one remonstrance, she leaned forward, her eyes intent on what she might see, while my hand enjoyed the delightful touch of green silk stretched over a beautifully modelled leg.

I turned from admiring the contours of the dark green leg to see what was happening to the pale blue ones. My hand, not being needed to see with, stayed where it was most comfortable. The blue legs had become most interesting. The skirt had been moved still more – the length of the blue stockings was now measurable. Not far above the knee they ended, and considerable evidence was to be seen of two plump, white thighs, with the hand of the lover tenderly touching and stroking them. The pale blue slippers now lay side by side, and the girl's two arms, while her legs were being so lovingly caressed, were tight about the neck of her lover, holding his face to hers for kisses.

'Peter!' warned Alice again, in a tense whisper. For, somehow, when I turned my eyes from the pretty green leg, my hand, left to its own resources without the guiding eye, had wandered somewhat; in fact, had strayed beyond the green stocking and was thrilling to the touch of soft, warm flesh. Alice stirred a bit, as if impatient, but it was satisfying to note that, in so doing, she thrust her legs still further from under her skirt. On looking to see what change her new attitude had effected, I was overjoyed to see that, right close at hand, there was a most enticing bit of plump, white thigh for me to appreciate. Close at hand, indeed my hand made haste to embrace its opportunity, in fact to grasp at the unseen, as it felt its unhindered way to discover yet undiscovered pleasures to the touch.

'Pete, look,' whispered Alice again. And we looked. Not fifteen feet away, the other pair, unsuspecting still, pursued their own amusement. The girl had moved – her skirt was drawn clear above her waist; her legs were all exposed, and her hips as well. Quite evidently the young lady had worn no panties or drawers! The young lover was sitting up, fussing with his clothing, his eyes enjoying a vision of loveliness. Those two pretty legs were slightly parted now, and such a dear little nest of hair was seen.

'Oh, Pete!' – Alice gasped this time. For, as the man's clothing was released, his sweetheart's hand reached out and took hold of something. The lover stretched out an instant, wriggled, and one bare, manly leg came out of his trousers – bare, that is, except for shoe and sock and red garter. This bare leg was then placed across another bare leg, the man's between the woman's two, the woman's between the man's, and, satisfied with this arrangement, the lover lay upon his sweetheart, his arms about her, hers about him. They moved delicately, as if rubbing on each other.

I had found Alice's hand and, by placing it in a certain position, I showed her that I, too, had something which might be held, should her hand care to hold it. Soon, indeed, she was holding it, and by playing with it as if absent-mindedly, she caused me no little pleasure. But her eyes she could not remove from the scene before us.

We could hear soft cooings and murmurs. Alice and I ceased to regard the others for a time. She came somehow closer into my arms, lay quite heavily there, in fact, and, in so placing herself, managed to arrange her clothing so that both her legs lay bare. To my real surprise, Alice, too, was guiltless of drawers or panties. Much reassured, I let my hands flow freely over the delicious surfaces of her thighs and hips. Our lips were fast together, and now I learned how Alice could kiss when really interested. When my hand, in its wanderings, encountered certain soft curls, her lips and her tongue assailed me with a quite impetuous ardour.

But curiosity drew my eyes again to the other lovers. 'Look, Alice!' I whispered to her, and, as we looked, our hands became very busy and our eyes drank in a most lascivious sight. Side by side now the girl and her man were sitting, all outer clothing removed from their waists down, and the girl had further so opened her blouse that her dainty breasts hung out. With one arm, each embraced the other, and their lips were crushed together. With their free hands they were playing with the most delicious playthings that the hands of man and of woman can touch. The man's hand was moving between his sweetheart's parted legs; the girl's hand held something hard and stiff, which she manipulated gently.

'Oo-oo-oh!' gasped Alice, and fell to kissing me wildly. Needless to say, I kissed wildly back. Her hand held something hard and stiff, and her treatment of it was as skilful as it was delicious. My hand was between her lovely legs, and the manner in which she received its ministrations showed that I had not forgotten how to play upon that organ which, if properly touched, causes a woman's body to re-echo with most delicious harmony.

Alice's lovely naked thighs lay exposed to my hands and eyes. But her intentions towards me were shown even more clearly now by her conduct. Somehow, at some time, Alice had had experience. She had learned how to be charmingly wanton without being shameless. Her kisses were delights of art and skill, her movements were delicate and yet effective, her grip on what her fair hand held was possessive without being painful, and her handling of it, without being obtrusive, was obviously intended ultimately to bring it between her legs.

'Pete, darling, look there!' Alice whispered between her kisses. Our lovers were at last in earnest, the man lying between the girl's legs which were embracing and holding him while he moved with vigorous thrusts of his hips. 'Peter!' cooed Alice, and 'Alice!' I cooed back – and somehow her weight was upon me, her legs spread far apart, and she took me into herself.

In the course of time we sat up again and looked about. The other pair were sitting up, smiling at us. We were discovered! In our excitement, we had moved so that our former shelter no longer concealed us. Strange to say, Alice did not seem concerned. Either she was accustomed to intimate acts of love with others – which I really do not believe – or else she saw at once that we must make the best of the situation and, perhaps, improve it. At any rate, she laughed quite gaily and stood up, shaking her skirt down to where it belonged. I stood up, too, but not so easily, as my trousers needed attention.

The other man called out, 'What luck?' 'Fine,' I said. 'A bull's-eye!' Alice laughed again. 'Same here,' he answered, stepping nearer. 'My name's Bill.' 'Mine's Pete.' And we shook hands. I presented Alice. She shook hands. 'Gladys,' said Bill, 'here's Pete and Alice – come and get acquainted.' So, all introduced, we sat down, Bill and Gladys on either side of me, and Alice on the other side of Bill. We talked a bit, about anything but the events of the past hour. But after a time, conversation waned. Bill was whispering to Alice, so I began to whisper to Gladys. What I said was of no importance to the other two, but it made Gladys laugh, with her eyes shining. Furthermore, she put out her hand to see if what I had told her was true. Finding that it was, she seemed satisfied and lay back, smiling enticingly. Somehow I found that I was embracing her naked legs. Bill did not seem to care – he was doing the same to Alice!

It was most interesting to play this way with another man's sweetheart while the other man played with mine. There lay Alice, who had just given me a delicious half hour, doing the same for Bill, and, believe me, I knew that Bill was lucky! And here lay Gladys, giving herself to my caresses as she had given herself to Bill not long before – and, believe me, I soon knew that both Bill and I were lucky, twice!

Gladys was not so voluptuously formed as Alice, but she knew her part and made every little movement have just the meaning that it should. Her little breasts were just as satisfactory to my hands and lips as Alice's fuller ones, and she responded just as delightfully to the skilful touch of my fingers. She was all woman, and ended by giving me a most glorious moment as I scored another bull's-eye. Unless all familiar signs failed, Gladys received as much pleasure from my success as I did. Bill scored his second centre shot almost at the same time. Both girls were flushed and radiant.

'Bill's bigger,' confided Alice in a whisper as she nestled up against me, 'but he hasn't your finesse, Peter darling. But it was wonderful to get that twice – oo-oooh!' Gladys was whispering to Bill, and I heard his heavier voice whisper back, 'I'm glad you liked it, honey' – so I guessed that Gladys told him she had been pleased.

Bill produced some liquid refreshment. I don't drink much, but it was awfully good whiskey, and the little glass went around among the four of us several times. The girls got just a little drunk, and I began to get interested. There is something about taking a girl who is just a little bit intoxicated that is most fascinating . Even the ardent ones become just a bit more so, and the movements of a girl on the way to becoming drunk are most wanton.

It wasn't so very long before all of us, stimulated a bit, were huddled in a most intimate group. The girls lay all over us two men and kissed us with wet lips. We fondled them and kissed them on the lips and on the nipples of their breasts, which they had left bare. The whiskey and these caresses soon had their effect. 'Pete, what's that?' Alice exclaimed, and made her eyes round with mock amazement. For there it was again, as large as ever! 'Gladys, see what I've found, see what I've found!' Alice called as she unfastened my trousers and held her discovery in her hand. Gladys, without a word, unbuttoned Bill and took out what she'd found. No doubt about it, Bill's was bigger. But the girls were each satisfied – I know we all four laughed at the picture: two very pretty girls, somewhat flushed with whiskey, their breasts bare, each sitting beside a recumbent man and holding in her hand something she never could claim as her own, except a man gave it to her. We all took another drink.

Alice was getting very gay, and her kisses more and more amorous. She handled me lovingly, and called me, or that part of me which her hand held, all sorts of amusing names. But I was surprised when, with a sudden change of position, she put her head down and began to kiss it. Gladys immediately did the same to Bill. We two men lay there awhile, too contented to speak, and watched our sweethearts kiss and suck us. Alice knew how to use her mouth! I have wondered, and have never found out, where and how she learned it.

Neither man nor woman could stand that for long. Gladys curled around and got her leg over Bill, and Alice imitated. I soon felt her, after a bit of rubbing, slide down upon me, hot and moist. The girls rode us so and rubbed upon us as we bounced them with our knees and hips. They laughed and exclaimed and crooned and cooed, each holding the other's hand as they jounced about side by side on their willing mounts, and they must have given each other some signal, for both sat erect at almost the same moment with that look of wondering delight that lovers love to see on their sweetheart's faces, and then collapsed together, gasping, as Bill and I rang up our third bull's-eyes!

It was now getting late. We all promised to meet again, and went our ways. On the road home, lying with her head against my shoulder as I drove, Alice made the most extraordinary remark I ever heard from her lips – 'Pete, I'm fucked to a frazzle!' Perhaps she was, then, but after a couple of cocktails and dinner at her house (friend husband being away), she invited me to her room, and there, on her own bed, and all naked this time, both of us, at her own request, I – well, the lady used the word first – fucked her again!

And then she lay there, smiling, stretched out so beautifully and happily naked, and I tenderly kissed her good night and goodbye. And I still recall that day with passionate desire.

Cunts   Pretty young women have nice ticklish little cunts between their legs for ardent young men to put stiff pricks into. Let any young man see a young woman's pretty, hairy cunt, and watch how his prick will come up standing! If a girl will sit with her legs apart, and then pull her dress up, uncovering lovely soft white thighs and the delicious little hairy place between them, any young man's prick will get hard and stiff, and eager to come close and touch the soft young cunt.

Think of all the pretty cunts between young women's legs as they walk about the streets, or lie asleep at night, and all the manly pricks covered up in trousers. What joy when one of the cunts and one of the pricks come together! In dancing, with bodies held close together, prick and cunt are near each other. It is not strange that young women and men learn to desire each other and want to go from dancing to lie together somewhere – even if they do not say so!

What a pleasure to meet at a dance in the country some girl who knows the delights of fucking, who will go gladly from the hot, noisy room, where her desires have been aroused by the closeness of your body to hers, to some quiet, cool, dark corner of the woods and there lie down and open her receptive cunt to the thrusts of your eager prick! It is a joy to find such a girl, press your body to hers in the rhythm of a delightful waltz, feel her arms tighten, and know that, as you touch her legs in the dance, her cunt is beginning to twitch and tingle. Hold her close and let her feel the pushing and throbbing of your prick as it begins to get stiff from feeling the warmth of her body through the clothing. Then take her outside and kiss her until she opens her mouth and clings to you in the delirious kiss that means surrender. After that, put your arms about her, and walk up the road to the pitch-black grove. She will know for what you are going there, and will stop you on the way for more and more ardent kisses, holding you close and rubbing her body against yours. In the darkness of the grove, she will let you feel her young breasts, firm under your caressing hand, and will press against you with her legs. She will stand with her back against a tree and let you lean against her and kiss her more, and as you raise her dress, she will part her legs so that your fingers will find her hot young cunt, moist and open. How she will tremble and thrill as your fingers play with that lovely, hairy organ! She may put her hand on you, and find your prick all hard and stiff and throbbing, and take it out and put it between her legs, and even make you fuck her that way, leaning against a tree!

Or she may sink to the soft ground, drawing you down to her, and lie there with her legs far apart, her cunt ready and open, and take you with sucking kisses, gasping and shaking with desire, her whole body enjoying the delicious fucking you will give her. And through the darkness you will hear the soft sounds of other happy couples, not far off, all aroused by the dance, enjoying their fucking-play in the soft night.

But even in cities there are cunts that like to be fucked. If you know a full-blooded young woman, a young married woman who is keen, or a young widow who has not had a man for some time, take her out to a good dinner and, after a few drinks, drive her in your automobile to some quiet street in the suburbs and stop at some secluded spot away from the lights.

Take her in your arms and kiss her, and she will be glad. If she is just drunk enough, or careless enough, and you are skilful, she will become so aroused with desire that she will let you take her in the back seat of your automobile and there give her the good fucking she longs for. Let your trousers down and sit there with your legs stretched out, and put her soft little hand on something big and hard. She will gasp and pull up her skirt and put herself astride you, and let her quivering cunt come down for a delicious, satisfying fuck on your stiff prick.

Best is a discreet young widow or divorced woman who has learned the delights of fucking and must indulge herself every few weeks. By waiting a month or so between times, she becomes so eager to feel a manly prick thrusting between her legs that she will not hesitate at all to let a suitable man know, by unmistakable signs, that she longs for a good fucking. Her cunt wants to be tickled and pushed and crowded by a nice thick prick, and if you are the man who meets with her favour at the time, she will give you the opportunity to take her and fuck her to the delighted satisfaction of both of you.

One summer I met a young divorced woman, who soon showed that she liked me. I used to call at her apartment for tea. We often kissed, and she kissed warmly, but I withheld myself, curious to see what she would do. I knew that she desired me, and she knew that I desired her. One afternoon, after we had had our tea and a few highballs, and a few ardent kisses, she excused herself and left the room. After a few minutes, she called to me. I found her in the half-opened doorway to her bedroom, clad only in a most delicious diaphanous pink silk nightdress, through which her beautiful body glowed, blushing. Without a word, I carried her to the bed and there, naked, we enjoyed hours of the most delightful fucking, until both of us were quite excited.

There are so many pretty little cunts that ought to be fucked every now and then, and there are so few of them that get as much delicious fucking as they should have. Young women mistakenly keep their cunts secreted and never use them, unless perhaps they finger them themselves, or let other women finger them or rub them sometimes. Such innocent diversions are better than nothing, of course, but to enjoy all the pleasure their cunts can give them, women ought to let themselves be fucked. Of course, there is danger in promiscuous fucking. But if a girl is discreet, and careful to associate with clean young men and see that proper precautions are taken, she can get a good satisfying fucking now and then with no danger at all. A girl can easily show a young man what she wants without being too bold, and if he is any sort of young fellow at all, he will be more than glad to give it to her. Think, ladies, of the thrill of knowing that 'it' is going to happen to you! You will be scared at first, when he comes to you, but if he is a decent fellow, he will soon love you and kiss you, and hold you close, and play with you, so that in a very short time you will be kissing him back, and clinging to him, and wanting him to love you more. And you will not mind, then, when he puts his hands on your legs. How good it will feel to have his hands touching your bare legs, coming closer and closer to your cunt! Let him finger you for a while and fondle you there, and you will want him so much that you will be glad and excited to see his long, hard prick come out. Then lie back and surrender yourself to him, open your bodice so that he may play with your breasts, pull up your dress, put your legs apart, let him come in between them and put his prick in your cunt – then close your eyes as the dear lad fucks you. As you lie there, with your body held tight in his arms, you think, 'At last I am being fucked as a woman, and a man is fucking me! His hard prick is actually in my cunt, and this delicious sensation I feel as he pushes and thrusts is his big, loving prick fucking my cunt. Women, after you have been once fucked by a nice, lovely man with a big, thick prick, you will enjoy living and nothing in the world will give more satisfaction than letting your cunt be used now and then – not too often – for a sweet, delicious fucking.

I Want a Woman   I am alone, a stranger in a strange city. I see women all around me, passing on the streets, but they are all strangers. Among them are painted faces and glances of invitation, but I do not want a whore, a drunken, diseased thing; I want a clean, wholesome, laughter-loving woman with a taste for a little adventure with a clean, wholesome man.

I am a clean, wholesome man! I have batted around a bit, but I have kept my self-respect and have had nothing to do with prostitutes. But I have a man's appetite for a woman's body and have loved from time to time many women who have felt free to love me and to take the pleasure I could give them. By the freedom of their bodies, they've given me pleasure too. I have found them charming women, too, and quite able to maintain their positions as ladies – yes, and as good wives and mothers, too, in some cases – while doing as they pleased in the matter of getting a little extra enjoyment out of life by a night or two with me now and then.

I have been months now without the sight of a woman, except in public places. I have been continent too long – I want a woman all to myself to play with, to have play with me, to enjoy, and to give pleasure to. I find myself lying awake at night, thinking about the kind of woman I should enjoy. I do not want a young girl or a virgin. I do not like green fruit. I have heard of men who enjoy nothing but virgins, but that has always seemed to me a perverted taste. A young girl's maidenhood should be taken from her only under the most romantic circumstances, in the tender flush of young love. Otherwise, she is spoiled forever. For a full-grown man to take maidenheads, captured or bought for the purpose, is gross brutality. I have taken but one in my life, and that was my wife's and I do not recall that I, or she either, got much pleasure from the taking of it.

No, I want a woman whose virginity is gone, who is ripe for love, with enough experience to meet a man part way in the game. A woman about twenty-five (I am forty), a young wife or widow, or a bachelor maid who has not ruined her physical life by prizing virginity too highly, preferably one who has not borne children, who has kept the firm breasts of the young childless woman.

Well, supposing I have her, how would I wish to take her? I'll tell you. Assuming that we have become acquainted to the point at which we begin to understand each other – at which she begins to feel that I desire more of her than just her company at dinners and dances, and I begin to see that she is willing to give me more – assuming, then, that we understand each other, I would ask her to dine with me, and after making it quite clear (in a delicate way, of course) during our dinner that I am anxious to know her better, I would have her dance with me. In dancing it is possible for a man and woman to exchange certain confidences without saying a word. Being assured by certain little answering pressures, when I press her close in the dance, that she is willing to go further, I would suggest a taxi drive, and in the taxi, would try her out further by a few gentle caresses. If she permits my hand to clasp her leg above the knee, she will allow me to draw her to me and kiss her, and if she gives me back an open-mouthed kiss, it only remains to set the date for a night of more intimate delights.

I have a very secluded little bungalow in which, when the time comes, I bring her very discreetly after dark, in my own car. She takes off her cloak, and I lead her into my living room, where there is a cheerful log burning, with a great, comfortable couch in front of it. She is just a little excited perhaps, and I bring cocktails. Now, it is a fact that I like a woman just a little bit tipsy – not drunk, but with three or four drinks in her so that she is the least bit intoxicated. I usually find it easy to get them to that point – if they come with me at all, they will drink and enjoy it.

As we sit side by side, drinking our cocktails, I allow myself some familiar caresses and kisses. She answers readily to the kisses and soon responds warmly to the caresses. If she is just about drunk enough, it will be fun now to put my hand into her bodice and feel her breasts – firm, well-rounded, delicious to the touch – and, kissing her ardently, I then unfasten her clothing so that her breasts are exposed. Wonderful things, a woman's breasts, round, soft, white, with beautiful rosy nipples, warm, delicate! I love them more than any other part of a woman. I sometimes think that I could get entire satisfaction from a woman just by having the freedom of her breasts with my hands and lips. I confess I have never tried it, as I have never had to stop there. In fact, if a man gets to the point of having a woman bare her breasts to him, he will not be allowed to stop there!

There she lies, in a corner of my couch, in the firelight, her clothing disordered, her breasts in my hands, beneath my lips. I kiss them and nibble until she begins to stir with desire. Her hands caress my head, she lies back with her eyes closed, little tremors go through her, and she begins to murmur terms of endearment. I can now assure her that I love her, and I do so in ardent terms, moulding her breasts with my hands and covering her lips with kisses. She returns the kisses with her out-turned lips.

Still crowded against her as she lies back upon the pillows in the corner of the couch, I put my hand beneath her skirt. I clasp her calf, her knee; I stroke and fondle her legs, moving higher, higher, and I soon have my hand on her naked thigh. Continuing to kiss her madly and press against her, I fondle and caress the warm, soft skin, moving up her thigh to her hip, then to the soft, curly hair that grows above the junction of her legs. Tickling and lightly touching the soft curls, my fingers proceed gradually, gently, down between her legs, and touch and tickle there until, of her own accord, she parts her legs a little and lets my whole hand find and clasp what is between them.

After a few minutes' delicious play of fingers there, during which she lies quite passive, except for the uninterrupted sucking of her kisses and an occasional pressure of her hands, I begin with one hand to undo my clothing. As soon as she sees my purpose, she begins to loosen hers. I leave her now; her adoring eyes follow me as I mix another drink and bring it to her. This is a stiff one, but she drinks it down thirstily. Then I draw her to her feet and whisper to her that I want her naked. I lead her to a screened corner, and returning to the couch, lay off my own clothes and sit down to wait.

~ 15 ~

The Devil's Advocate

ROBERT SEWALL 1942

The Devil's Advocate by 'Wood C. Lamont' is arguably the finest and hottest erotic novel ever written and published in America. Yet it is today little known to the reading public, and then for the most part only in its abridged, rewritten form.

This novel is an erotic mystery. Unlike *Crimson Hairs*, which was a hard-boiled detective thriller in the Mike Hammer tradition, *The Devil's Advocate* is a more sophisticated, psychological tale, with character studies as important to the book as its hard-core action. It reads in the style of Dashiell Hammett, and in fact brings to mind Raymond Chandler's *The Big Sleep*, but with all the sex explicit, rather than just implied.

The plot is simple enough. A young woman, Clara Reeves, approaches a New York district attorney, Conrad Garnett, to enlist his aid in finding her missing older sister, Rita. The few available clues indicate that the missing woman was deeply involved in an organised ring of illicit sex and perversion, willingly participating in wild orgies on a regular basis. The district attorney suggests that the only way to find the sister is to follow the trail of clues, and journey themselves through the same sexual underground Rita seems to have disappeared into. After some persuasion and 'practice' with the help of the district attorney, Clara agrees, and like an Alice in a sexual Wonderland, is lead through an odyssey of increasingly bizarre sexual adventures. Some of the scenes written by the author are unique in the annals of erotica; no one who has read the unexpurgated 'pony scene' will ever forget it!

What makes *The Devil's Advocate* so exceptional is the quality of the writing. The characters and their motives and development are completely believable. The author's facility with words allows him to paint pictures so vivid that the reader can easily visualise the action, as if personally present to experience the sights and sounds and smells first hand. Even the construction of the mystery itself is engrossing, making it difficult to put down the novel once it has been started.

There was more mystery to this novel than what was just in the plot. When first published in 1942, those in the know saw the slyness in this rather obvious *roman-à-clef*. The give-aways were hard to miss. The author's name 'Wood C. Lamont' was in fact a thinly disguised attempt to implicate as author the then popular poet and *litterateur* Clement Wood, a point reinforced by the book's dedication, 'For Whom But Gloria', Gloria being the name of Wood's wife! Members of the New York literary and publishing world must have chuckled (or shuddered as the case might be) as they read the sex scenes, for those scenes were not so much the product of a 'dirty' creative mind, but the vivid recollections of actual orgies that had taken place at Wood's country estate, Bozenkill, orgies many of them had participated and been photographed in! How many of the then power élite saw themselves in the pages of *The Devil's Advocate* can only be guessed; today only a few old timers can still tell you the real identities of the novel's cast of characters.

Who then were the culprits behind this wonderful, sexy, nasty book? That is no longer a secret. The original author of the book has been identified as Robert Sewall, a man described by Gershon Legman (the world's foremost authority on erotic folklore, and no slouch on the entire genre of erotica) as 'a talented young American, exceptionally gifted at pastiche' (*The Horn Book*, 1964, p. 36). Legman should know, for it was he himself who recruited Sewall into writing erotic novels for money in the early 1940s, at a time when Legman no longer had time to do this himself. The book's appearance was purely a function of its time, for the advent of World War II caused a drastic change in the production of erotica. No longer could books be printed at Depression prices. Raw material needed for manufacture was rationed, and presses were busy with war-related activity. The erotica publishers were inventive if nothing else, and soon came to self-publish their books with the aid of the mimeograph. Books could be entirely produced in a small room with no expensive equipment and in complete secrecy. All that was needed was a manuscript, a typist to make a stencil, and paper to put through an inked machine. Binding was frequently nothing more than pages sewn together with heavy twine.

Thus it was that *The Devil's Advocate* saw the light of day in 1942, a 200-page book, perhaps in an edition of 100 copies, mimeoed one side of the page only, its cover red construction paper with the head of a devil (designed by a New York City court clerk who had copied the image from an RCA record catalogue). It had been physically produced in the basement of the Chrysler Building, in the shop of a bookman named Herman Miller, who was also reprinting other erotic books during the war by mimeo to satisfy his clientele. The book quickly sold out; those lucky enough to have it rented it to others, sometimes for as much as $50 a week! *The Devil's Advocate* was instantly (in)famous.

The cause of all this notoriety was however not the book Robert Sewall remembered writing! Unbeknownst to the author, the typist hired to make the stencil for the mimeo machine had decided to edit and embellish the novel, and to expurgate some of the more flagrant sadomasochistic scenes. This typist was none other than Gershon Legman! Upon seeing the first edition of *The Devil's Advocate*, Sewall sat down and rewrote the story as he remembered penning it. This 'author's' version came out, again from the basement of Herman Miller, in 1944, but as a one-hundred-and-forty-page book entitled *The Sign of the Scorpio* by 'Bruce Abbot'. Although most of the action of the 1942 edition was still present, the skilful mastery of words and composition was missing, and through the years, it has been this abridged, rewritten version that has been reprinted, while the superior first appearance has become all but lost.

The following excerpt is taken from a unique, original typescript of the first (1942) edition of *The Devil's Advocate*. Clara Reeves has invited the district attorney back to her home so he can see the evidence she has so far discovered. What follows is undercover work of the most literal type!

～ from *The Devil's Advocate*

She came toward him as though she were going to kiss him, and he involuntarily reached, or half-reached, his arms toward her. But she merely took his hat and put it away. She moved as lightly as a breath, and she made him feel no longer earthbound just to watch. He followed her into the living room, jealous of the light summer dress which clung possessively to her young body.

'Will you have a gin rickey?' she asked. 'It's so warm this evening.'

'Yes, thanks. Can I help?'

'You can squeeze the lemons.'

Standing beside her as they mixed the drinks, he was already drunk on her smell – the heady aura of young sweat and soap, good perfume and clean cunt. His glance dropped to her breasts; his mind already between her thighs.

'No news from your sister?' he asked.

'Nothing.'

'Now don't be so gloomy about it. You'll hear from her. I promise you.'

'Let's have our drinks out on the terrace? It's nice out there.'

They sat looking out over the old, enormous garden. He rested his glass on the arm of the wicker chair and watched her through half-closed eyes as she rested in the beach chair. A breeze rustled through the dusk as the moon rose suddenly on the horizon. The breeze toyed with her dress, and promised to play interesting tricks if he would be patient.

'This was my parents' house,' she said. 'Aunt Madge got it through my father's will with the understanding that it was to go to us. It's really way too big for just two girls. We have to keep two maids. I'd rather have just a little apartment.'

The breeze had lifted her skirt just as Clara uncrossed her legs. Unnoticed by her in the increasing dark, her dress lay across her thighs, above her rolled stockings. Her knees, dimpled and round, smiled at the District Attorney. He sipped his gin and appreciated as hard as he could, pitting his eyesight against the dusk. Had the girl's legs been covered, nothing unnatural would have been noticeable in her posture. But with her legs bare where her skirt had gently fallen back, she appeared to have taken a suggestive position. Her knees were turned slightly outward, and the inner sides of her thighs made it seem that more was being shown than actually was.

Conrad said something to her. While he was speaking she drew one knee up. He finished his sentence, looking directly into her eyes; and nothing in his manner indicated that he had noticed anything out of the ordinary. But the whole underside of her leg, the side toward him, was bare to his sight from knee to buttock. It hung there like a gigantic, ripe, unbelievable – and, for a fact, somewhat ill-proportioned – pear. It was funny how much there was to a woman's leg, and what you usually see even when a dress flies up in running or getting on a bus is just nothing compared to the whole length of ham and thigh that there is to it. Her skin was pink under a coating of tan, and he could even see the line of lighter colour where her bathing suit no doubt kept her upper thigh from tanning. Where the naked leg joined its twin on the seat there was – there was – no, it was growing dark, and there was nothing. Conrad sighed, but continued to make light conversation while enjoying the full pleasure of the juniper berry and the partial pleasure of the flesh.

Clara wanted to talk about her sister Rita, and circumstances being what they were, naturally you sat there and let her talk. But when the breeze which had been friendly before turned spiteful and carried her skirt down again, and she, feeling some movement of her dress, covered her legs entirely, he was tired of the terrace. He rose, and Clara jumped from her chair.

'We'll go in,' she said. 'I'll show you what I found.'

Inside she said, 'Shall I bring the drawer down or would you rather see it just as I found it? I suppose that would be best. It's in her bedroom upstairs.'

He followed her up the stairs, stifling with an effort a sudden urge to run his wrist up between the legs that were just in front of his nose. Run his wrist up and get it all dripping wet in her cunt. But it would startle her, he realised, and she would probably be bone-dry there anyhow. Docilely, then, he followed her into her sister's bedroom. Clara un-locked a bureau drawer with a nail file – her expertness showed that she had been in that drawer more than once since discovering its contents.

'I could put the drawer on the bed if you want to look at it,' she said. He agreed.

'First of all,' he said, 'we have . . .'

'Oh, these are mine!' Clara exclaimed, snatching from his hand a pair of light green silk panties which lay atop a thick morocco-bound book. She hustled the panties into a closet and came back and sat by him.

'I thought this was Rita's drawer,' he suggested.

'I was using that old silk thing as a dustcloth on the day I discovered this,' she explained lamely. She was rosy with blushes, and Conrad eyed her with some amusement. He could almost see her wondering whether it was true that hair grows on your palm if you play with yourself and then everybody can tell. But he tried to remain noncommittal.

'Yes,' he said. 'A dustcloth. I see.'

He returned to his inspection of the drawer, and began laying the objects on the bed. He put down the black book and picked up a smaller one in padded ivory leather with a ridiculous little miniature lock that did not lock. Rita's diary. The handwriting was soft and curling. An envelope of silk with a Chinese letter on it in red brush strokes. Contents – Clara averted her eyes – six condoms of extraordi-nary good manufacture, printed in gay colours and curiously armed with an array of rubber spikes, knobs, dimples, nipples, fins, studs, tiny fingers, whiskers and bits of sponge. One book of etchings, hand tinted with watercolours; scorpion bookplate at the front. A glance was sufficient to explain the type of etchings these were. The workmanship was sumptuous, though. His eyes lingered for a moment on one etching of two girls 69ing while they swung through the air, supported by flying rings in which the one with her head down had hooked her knees. Clara could not resist peeking to see which drawing had struck his notice. He looked up suddenly and she swallowed hard.

Next came a small *bocca-da-gazza* case of shantung silk with a bone clasp. Inside were two silver balls of a size somewhat smaller than a walnut. They rang gaily when Conrad shook the box gently. Clara looked puzzled, but he knew she was too shy to ask for an explanation. 'Japanese,' he said, '*rinne tama* set.' Clara nodded brightly as though she really knew what the hell he was talking about. Then three small volumes, each with the now familiar scorpion bookplate: *Memoirs of Madame Condeux*, *Sixty-Nine Delightful Ways to Sin*, *The Art of the Tongue* and *Ten Inches Above the Garter*. The last two were combined in one volume, illustrated with photographs. After this came an object which was, yet was not, a male sex organ. It was a rubber replica, excellent in proportion and design, hollow rather than solid and therefore extremely lifelike to the touch, and made to fit standards which were indeed exacting, at least as to size. Its workmanship was, indeed, its fault. It was too real. Even the colouring was perfectly human. Every vein was indicated, every nuance of tan and pink and red. Clara's cheeks were crimson.

Finally there was a small cat-o'-nine tails, but with only five tails. It was of the finest and softest leather – kidskin certainly, Conrad was sure – wound and braided by a master hand, tooled and worked with a wealth of fine design. Beside this there was a small silver box, not unlike a snuffbox, and holding a quantity of broken greenish-black shreds not unlike tea.

'Cannabis,' said Conrad, sniffing it.

'What?' Clara asked.

'Hm? Oh – a – a sort of Indian tobacco. We'll have to try some of it sometime. It's hard to get because of the tax.'

They sat in the midst of Rita's secret sex life, like two castaways amidst their ship's debris, and they said nothing.

'What do you make of it all?' she finally asked.

'It's very interesting,' said Conrad. 'Very. But I don't know that it proves anything much. But there's the diary – you read it, didn't you?'

Clara nodded. He picked it up and rifled through the pages, finally selecting one and knitting his brows over it. He handed it to Clara. 'I don't seem to be able to make out the handwriting,' he said. 'Would you read me a couple of pages?'

'Oh, but really!' Clara remonstrated. 'Why, the words are just so – so – I just couldn't!'

'Come now, don't be silly,' he said firmly. 'How else can we investigate this thing?' He moved some of the objects aside and sat down beside her, handing her the book. 'Here, begin with this entry.'

' "It was wonderful last night," ' Clara began in a low voice after a hesitant moment. ' "It was more wonderful than ever, just as it always seems to be." ' Clara stopped uncertainly.

'Go on,' Conrad said. 'That's very good. I couldn't make out a word of that myself.'

' "I went to his apartment. He was waiting for me," ' Clara recommenced, her voice now determined but still a bit quavery. ' "We didn't say a word, but he kissed me as soon as I was in the door. When he did that our bodies touched, and I knew that he had been thinking of me for I felt – felt . . ." '

'Go on,' said Conrad. 'What's the matter?'

'I can't read that word.'

He took the book from her hands and studied it. ' "Prick",' he said; ' "felt his prick". She says she felt his prick. Go on.'

'But I can't read words like that out loud to you.'

He took her hand. 'Dear, sweet girl,' he said tenderly. 'I'm sorry to have to ask you to do this. But your innocence will keep such words from actually touching you. I'm the only one who hears you say them, and I know that it is not you who is saying them, but Rita. You must be Rita's voice for me, Clara, if we are to learn what has happened to her. Every word in this diary may be important to us.'

'I'll try,' Clara said. Conrad patted her knee, and then patted her above the knee. ' "I knew that he had been thinking of me, for I felt his – prick pressing against my belly. We fairly ran into the living room, and there, before that great Chinese Buddha, I pulled off my things. I shook the snow from my coat and then I stripped, from my coat to my skin, without once pausing. My darling simply stood and stared while I peeled off my clothes, for I was in a perfect fury to be rid of them, and have him on me instead. Still, I remembered how he likes to see me in the various progressive stages of undress, and I took time to let him see everything nice that there was to see about each stage. I looked back over my shoulder while I took off my snow boots with the white fur rills after my coat and dress and underwear were off, and how his eyes were shining. I knew he could see my pussy between the cheeks of my bottom, and he loves that. Men are so silly.

' "As soon as I was stark naked I ran to the fire that was burning in the grate and stood by it, pretending to warm my behind. I wasn't merely pretending, though, for it was really terribly cold outside. Then he came to me and said that he would warm it for me, so I got a footstool and bent across it and had him caress my behind. That warmed both of us! Then, when he had finished, he threw a log into the fire and took off his clothes.

' "I lay at his feet adoring him while he undressed. My bottom was burning and my cunt itched like fire. For a girl like me it's so wonderful to belong to a man so thoroughly! As soon as he would let me, I pulled myself to my knees and began to kiss his thighs and his belly and his prick. But he wouldn't let me put it in my mouth then, no matter how much I begged him. He took me to the sofa and we stretched out on it side by side, our bellies touching, and he teased me with his cock for a while. I thought he was never going to let me have it, but at last he allowed me to hold it in my hand and play with it, and soon I was holding it warmly between my legs against the hair of my pussy, and in just a little while then it began to tickle me inside my cunt with the tip. I was anything but cold by this time, but I was shivering I was so passionate, and he teased me, asking me if I wanted more of a fire, so I said yes. I was only joking, but he took me seriously, and went to fetch another log. I could see his cock standing there so stiff and up like a hat rack every time I lifted my head and looked back, and the fire in my eyes seemed to make him wild. I was on fire inside too, and I could hardly wait for him to leap on me. I threw my legs open and turned over on to my belly. My cunt was so wet and excited that the juice flowed all over my leg down to my knee, and the couch was dripping wet. He threw himself into the saddle and into my cunt he went, just as hard as he could. By that time his prick was simply bursting out of its skin like an overdone hot dog, and he fucked me like a beast. I could see that he was no more thinking of me as who I was than I don't know what." '

Clara looked up questioningly at Conrad.

'Just confused writing,' he explained airily, 'the recollection probably excited her.'

' "I was just a cunt to him then",' Clara continued. ' "I could do nothing but lay there on my back with my legs around him and my hands helping him – one hand squeezing his balls and the other hand on his behind the way he likes so much and that makes him come like a torrent. I loved him with all my body and soul. I came again and again, and the whole room swam around me. It was like a forest fire spinning out all over me from inside my cunt and from my burning bottom. I clutched at his balls so hard and dug my fingers into his bottom so fiercely that I must have hurt him with my nails. But I didn't care. It was glorious. At last I felt his cock burst into me like a torrent, and then the sperm bled down around his cock and out of me on to the sofa while he softened inside me."

' "Then, after he had fucked me, he let me suck it for a little while. I cleaned off all the sperm – I love to do that so I have the taste in my mouth for hours until I drink coffee and cut it – and sucked the sweat off his balls. I got his cock in my mouth and was pumping it up and down to try to raise another hard-on so he would fuck me again, but he said that I was too eager and took it away from me. Then he told me to pick up my clothes and his for we were going upstairs to bed and fuck all night like a couple of minks." '

'Let's not bother with the upstairs part just now,' Conrad suggested. 'Why Clara, you're trembling! What's the matter?'

'I just can't believe it,' she said weakly. 'That my own sister – Rita – that she'd – that she would . . . ' His shoulder was there to lean on, so lean against it she did. His arm went around her. It was very cosy and warm. Her breasts felt funny and the nipples stung. 'I don't know what you must think of me,' she added after a moment.

'But why in the world? You haven't done any of these things, have you?' he asked.

'Oh no! No! Never! Why I've never even thought of them!' She looked up at him with dewy eyes. 'You do believe me, don't you? I never even heard of things like that until I found out what was in this drawer.'

'But you do think about them now? Now that you've found out?' He infused a persuasively sympathetic note into his voice. His eyes roamed to where he had watched her hide the panties they had found in the drawer, and her eyes followed his guiltily.

'I – I can't help thinking about it sometimes. And those books – the funny, terrible things that are in those books!'

Conrad drew her gently toward him and downward. Together they settled back and Clara, to her surprise, discovered in a faraway sort of recognition, that she was lying side by side with the district attorney on the bed. She would have thought more about it, but she was busy noticing the funny swath of gray-white hair that cut through for a few inches on the side of his head. It was so distinguished. He soothed her and caressed her, and before she knew it she had been kissed, and her lips had been forced open to accept the tip of a serpentine, searching, red tongue. She was a little shocked but something made her touch the tip of his tongue with the tip of hers, timidly at first and then more and more responsively as he sucked the passion up into her mouth. Her mind suddenly took control again and she pulled her lips away from his, her cheeks flaming with shame. But he did not let her think about that long.

'You know,' he told her, patting her hip, 'I have a plan that I think will lead to your sister so we can get her away from whoever is influencing her in this way. There's a bare chance, I suppose, that she may return, but from what we read in that diary I imagine she likes it wherever she is. We'll just have to find her – you'll have to find her, I should say.'

'What do I do?' she asked.

'Well, if there is such a person as this Scorpion you talk about – and I'm saying that without having heard all of Rita's diary; you'll have to read all the rest of it to me, you know – well then he'll be very anxious not to have that ring lying around, now that Rita has disappeared. So tomorrow we'll run an ad in the paper saying that such a ring has been found. If he shows up, perhaps you can find out something about him.'

'And find out where those horrible orgies are that Rita mentions in her diary!'

'Yes, and where she is now,' he finished. 'But you'll have to have nerve, Clara. And – well, he may take a fancy to you – '

'You mean I'd have to . . . '

'Yes, Clara, you would. He may want to make love to you. You're so fresh and young and vital. Why a man would have to be made of stone – and this Scorpion is anything but inhibited. If you met him; if he took you somewhere in a car, perhaps, he would want to kiss you, to hold you tightly like this . . . '

'How awful!' Clara exclaimed.

'And he would probably squeeze your thigh, too. Like this. Then he would kiss you again.' He kissed her till he felt her grow limp in his arms. He found her young breasts and pressed them hungrily. His fingers worked in through the neck of her dress and softened one fruit-like titty as an orange is softened to pulp. 'He might even want to fuck you, Clara,' he said.

'He wouldn't!' She was so violent in her outburst that she threw Conrad's hands from her and sat up.

'But if finding Rita depended on it?' he asked gently.

She bit her lip and tried to look resolute. 'Well – I love my sister. I suppose I'd do anything to find her and bring her back. But I've never done anything like that. I – I – well, yes, I would though. To get Rita back, I'd let him do anything he wanted.'

'I don't think you could. I don't think you could even undress in front of a man without dying of shame. Could you undress in front of me now?'

'But nothing depends on it now.'

'No, but when it does you won't be able to cope with the situation, I'm afraid. Maybe we'd better turn the matter over to the police. You're willing to help, but I don't think you could go through with it. Timidity, you know. After all you're a virgin.'

'I would not be timid! Not if getting Rita back depended on it. I have plenty of nerve, I do.'

'Nerve enough to pretend that I'm this Scorpion person? And that I've just told you that I won't help you if you don't undress to the skin this minute? That might be just what happens.'

'I have plenty of nerve,' Clara repeated. She made herself stand up. She was blushing, and she was trembling. The DA was trembling too, but not as noticeably.

She unbuttoned her dress at the front. It was belted, and she took the belt off, and there was a zipper placket at the side that she unfastened. Her skin showed through pinkly between the edge of her brassière and the waist of her panties as seen through the open zipper now. 'Do you really want me to undress?' she faltered, hoping for a final reprieve. He shrugged as though to say, 'I told you you didn't have the nerve,' and she closed her lips tightly and gathered folds of her dress in her fists, raising it over her bare thighs to her hips. He saw the lacy panties that he had only imagined before on the terrace. Then she took the dress off over her head with crossed arms, tugging to pull the tight-fitting cloth past the gorgeous bulge of her breasts.

Her underthings – what there was to them – fitted her like a dream. But even a dream was superfluous on her. At his nod she unfastened the brassière, but she did it the hard way, slipping the straps off first and slowly reaching behind her with one hand to undo the snap, but by then one nipple had peeped out. The brassière fell away along her arms. Her breasts were terribly young, the tips pouting upward and the flesh firm and high but with a rich groove between them. They were the golden colour of melons and as round. Conrad smiled wolfishly. 'You have more nerve than I thought,' he told her, by way of encouragement.

Clara bent to take off one shoe, and her breasts swung forward like temple bells, slowly and resplendently. It made her ashamed, they seemed so alive, so the other shoe she took off by lifting her foot up and back to one side and reaching down. The movement raised her breasts this time, and Conrad's palms went sweaty with wanting to reach for them without waiting. But he restrained himself. He couldn't risk frightening the quarry. Not when she was almost within reach already. With Conrad possession was a thrill, of course, but the thrill of the chase was better. A fuck was a fuck most of the time, but to seduce an innocent young girl who was obviously just waiting to be seduced but fought against it half-heartedly – there was a game.

With her shoes off Clara looked even smaller and more helpless. And the gesture of unrolling her stockings and pulling them off was exciting less because it revealed the hair of her cunt under the edge of her panties than because it made her handle her own naked thighs, and made her more aware of her increasing nakedness before a man's eyes. She leaned against a chair, and, turning her face away from Conrad's, she pulled off her lace panties with three quick gestures, sliding her palms down along her sides under the elastic band at her waist, pushing the clinging material down along her thighs and stepping out.

She did not try to hide the diamond patch of black hair at her crotch, although her hands fluttered a little as though she wanted to but was determined not to.

'You've never undressed before a man before, have you?' he asked softly.

'Never.' Her voice was even softer.

She went to him on the bed when he beckoned to her and sat down, covering her face with her hands. 'Have I nerve enough?' she asked. He did not answer, but gently made her lie down next to him while he rested by her on one elbow, looking down at her upturned face with the dry and frightened lips, and caressing her soothingly with his free hand.

He stroked her with his fingers from shoulder to knee, tickling her nipples, moulding her breasts, caressing her belly, poking between her tightly closed thighs. She tried to keep her arms drawn over her breasts to cover her nipples, although she did not seem to care about the dark blood red line of her slit which he could see at the jointure of her thighs. She puzzled him.

'Why do you let me do this to you?' he asked her, smoothing his hand over her firm young belly.

'Because you told me to,' she said. 'You wanted to see if I had nerve enough to meet the Scorpion, and I wanted to show you that I do, that's all.' She bit her lip. 'I'm awfully ashamed of myself,' she added. 'I wish you wouldn't look at me when you feel me, or feel me when you look at me. I feel terribly dirty.'

'Aren't you letting me do this because you want me to?'

'No, oh, no! I don't want you to do it at all. I want to go away in a corner and cry. I hate it.'

'Will you read some more of Rita's diary to me?' he asked. 'Will you lie here, naked the way you are right now, and read to me?'

'If you say I have to, I'will,' she answered, her eyes shut.

He gave her a book. It was not Rita's diary. It was the *Memoirs of Madame Condeux*. 'Read some of that to me,' he said. He moved closer to her, feeling her with his body as well as with his hands.

'Why are you doing this to me?' she asked him. Whatever was in her voice was not resentment. She was incredulous and she was ashamed, but not resentful.

'Because if you do find this Scorpion person,' he explained glibly, 'you'll probably find yourself obliged to do such shameful things – why, things you don't even know the existence of.' He was becoming a little thick-tongued with passion himself. 'If you're going to crack I want to know it right now, before we make any definite plans. If you break down and he finds out what you're up to, you may be in grave danger.'

'I told you I could do anything,' she said. Her voice was very small, and her hands trembled so much that he did not think it possible for her to read from the page, but she could read, and she did.

The Autobiography of a Flea 2
PAUL LITTLE 1968

They say that imitation is the highest form of flattery. That being the case, *The Autobiography of a Flea* is surely the most flattered example of erotica. Over the years it has managed to garner numerous translations and three 'sequels' (a record it co-holds with *The Way of a Man with a Maid*). Translations or sequels by the original artist (in any media) are rarely as good as the original work; the same by second parties hardly ever come close at all. Literature, like art, is too closely associated with the very basics of a person's personality to be imitated easily or well.

As was noted, mastery in the original *Autobiography of a Flea* (its record range of themes aside) was in its narrative form and skilful use of vocabulary, both polysyllabic and sexual slang. Its scenes were as graphic as any in English erotica, and its swear words were used not for shock effect, but because they perfectly fitted the activity described. The action was fast paced, and heavy on the sex acts. Character development was minimal, as were plot advancement and erotic realism.

Who then would dare to imitate so formidable a classic of erotica? The incentive would be clear – to capitalise on the fame and reputation of the original to enhance sales. (One would be a bit naïve to think that a sequel would be written out of altruistic adulation for the original author.) The person who dared was America's most prolific author of erotica, Paul Hugo Little.

Paul Little was a Chicagoan, an advertising executive and copy writer by trade. Equally he was the author of more than seven hundred works over a fifty-year period. Little had the great facility to write in any style or genre, and had a penchant for old erotica. Yet his 1960s erotica would never be confused with turn-of-the-century originals, for even when engaged in pastiche (as with sequels to *The Autobiography of a Flea*, *The Way of a Man with a Maid* and *Maud*

Cameron and her Gaurdian), his own distinctive style came through.

Little's *The Autobiography of a Flea 2*, is the first of three sequels he wrote for this title. It was first published in Atlanta, Georgia, in 1968, by Pendulum Books (a company owned by Mike Thevis, who was later imprisoned for his activities). The language and structure clearly lack the archaic flavour of the 1887 original. Additionally, where the original author, Stanislas de Rhodes, portrayed guilty, exploitative users and abusers of authority (and is tacitly judgemental of his characters), Little is more sympathetic with his subjects. His work has less sense of criminal activity and punition, and his actors seem genuinely to invite the sex play. He portrays them as engineers as well as victims of their fates and impulses and desires.

It would be easy to dismiss the Little sequel as a nondescript 1960s 'stroke-book' pretending to be heir to a great erotic classic. To our present eyes it lacks the unique language and form of its inspiration. But what will be the opinion a hundred years from now? Just as the original version has through the years gained respectability commensurate with its antiquity, so the same may again occur. The Little sequel is to say the least distinctive, if not distinguished, and perhaps the passing of a century will accomplish that metamorphosis. And after all, this novel could have been worse. Instead of being the work of a happy-go-lucky 'flea', it could have been the work of a 'louse'.

∼ from *The Autobiography of a Flea* 2

Father Lawrence approached the beautiful, tall Amazon. He put his hands on her hips and boldly appraised her swelling breasts with knowledgeable eyes. 'You seem very young, my daughter.'

'Alas, Father, I am twenty-eight. In Languecuisse, this is almost old age for a woman. The young men have eyes only for the damsels like that little Laurette you just met. She is nineteen, and that too is much older than is customary for the time of marriage in this region.'

'All the more reason for her being wed as soon as possible, and she will be,' Father Lawrence avowed. His hands slipped back now over Desirée's jutting, boldly ripe bottom cheeks, which he squeezed through her thin skirt. 'Of a truth, my daughter, you do not feel to be much older than Laurette yourself. And you tell me that there is no man hereabouts whom you deem sufficient to give you physical joy?'

'I said not so far, Your Reverence,' Desirée murmured.

She stared into his eyes, her red lips curving in a comprehending smile. And she moved closer to him, letting his hands wander as they would. Then she uttered a little gasp and looked down. Between their bodies, there was already a polarity: the cassock of the good Father bulged out tremendously from his loins. Furtively, the beautiful, chestnut-haired Amazon slipped her hand down to discover what this could signify, and her fingers tentatively closed over the protuberance.

'Oh, Your Reverence! I cannot believe it!' she ejaculated in a tremulous voice.

'What cannot you believe, my daughter?' His voice had hoarsened noticeably by this time, as might well be imagined. And his fingers grew bolder still, kneading and squeezing the luscious contours of Desirée's bottom through the thin stuff of her skirt.

'That you are such a man as heaven should have sent me long ago,' the Amazon brazenly murmured, looking deep into his eyes, her red lips moist and parted with obvious invitation.

'But things are not what they seem at all times, my daughter,' he banteringly replied. 'Perhaps it would be well to judge by actuality rather than by appearance.'

'But I would not dare offend Your Reverence,' Desirée apologetically murmured.

'That which is done sincerely is not offensive, my dear child,' he retorted.

At this, the forward young widow stooped, caught up the hems of his cassock and furled the silken garment to his waist, holding it there with one hand while she rummaged rather expertly at his drawers. In a trice she had liberated his sexual weapon, and her eyes widened with amazement at the sight.

Father Lawrence was prodigiously equipped. In full erection at her touch – for Desirée lost no time in clasping the middle of the shaft with her strong fingers to determine that it was in truth actuality and not appearance – his penis must have measured at least eight inches in length. It was admirably thick as well, and the head, which rose out of a narrow groove of circumcision, was oval-shaped and slightly elongated. Its lips were thin and tightly shut together, but they were already twitching with carnal irritation from the bold enclaspment of Desirée's beautiful hand.

'I cannot believe my eyes, Your Reverence,' she exclaimed, her voice slightly trembling. 'I truly would not have believed it!'

'Are you of a mind to test its measure, my daughter?' he softly enquired.

'Oh, yes, if Your Reverence would so honour a poor humble widow,' she breathed.

'Then you had best make the door sure, lest your new master come in upon us.'

'I will do that at once, Your Reverence. But do not worry about Père Mourier. He and the maiden Laurette will take a long and devious stroll before he reaches her abode, for he wishes to impress upon her the need for chastity. Besides, after he has gone to sleep, I will come to you again and we can have more time – that is, if I do not anger you by my sinfulness.'

'But you have committed no sin, my daughter. Yours is a curious inquisitiveness which both delights and inflames me.'

She hurried to the door and threw the bolt. Then, swiftly, she divested herself of her thin skirt and blouse, under which she was naked. She stood before him, hands on her sides, head tilted back, blushing deliciously, proud in the knowledge that his eyes roved over her sumptuous breasts, her suave, well-dimpled belly, the thick luxuriant garden of dark chestnut curls which covered her mound and disappeared between her thighs, and those robust yet beautifully proportioned thighs themselves, seemingly so capable of crushing a man's ribs in their fiery embrace.

With a gasp of admiration, Father Lawrence drew off his cassock and neatly hung it from a peg on the door of the little room which would shelter him this night. Taking off his shoes and divesting himself of his drawers, he stood before her equally naked, his body wiry yet vigorous, nowhere showing the emaciation or meagreness of age. And least of all did the fulminating structures of his swollen cock evince that flaccidity of the flesh which is so common to men who attain their two score of years and more. Desirée let a sigh of admiration escape her as she moved toward him, her big breasts jiggling with each step. Her nipples were already turgid coral points of erotic anticipation, and voluptuous shivers ran along her thighs and calves at the thought of what awaited her.

She put out one soft hand to cup his heavy, hairy balls, overcharged with amorous essence, and she exalted another sigh. Meanwhile, Father Lawrence, rather than let this judging be one-sided, circled her waist with his left arm and extended his right forefinger toward the thick bush of her pubis and began to feel for the soft pink lips of Venus themselves. Her slow little giggle and a lascivious squirming of her juicily rounded bottom cheeks told him that he had attained his objective. He began to rim the fleshy, soft and already moistening lips of her cunt with a lingering deliberation which at once told me, expert as I have become in such matters, that he was by no means a novice in the sweet games of Cythera.

Now she used both hands to cup and rub and massage the broad, hot, thickly veined shaft of his organ, and her breasts rose and fell with an erratic tumult as she conjectured just how that weapon would feel within her cunt.

'It is so big, so thick and hard and hot, Your Reverence!' she whispered. 'Do you really want to fuck me?'

'Once a sword is drawn, it must either draw blood or be sheathed satisfyingly,' he quipped. 'And since you are a widow, it follows that you are no virgin, and therefore my blade will not bleed you, my daughter. Let us proceed to sheath it, then, to your complete satisfaction.'

'Oh, yes, Your Reverence,' Desirée exclaimed.

Now it was his turn to use both hands as his fingers found the plump, palpitating lips of Desirée's cunt and drew them apart. Meanwhile, the beautiful chestnut-haired Amazon daintily put both forefingers on the sides of his cock and thus steered him toward her orifice. The naked, pink tip of his sword forced its way through the thick, curly ringlets which still shielded her secret bower, and then he gave himself a little forward jerk and engaged a good half of his shaft within her channel. Desirée uttered a cry of bliss: 'Oh, Your Reverence! It stretches me! It pierces me! Oh, do not stop now! Put all of it into me – quickly!'

'With the greatest of goodwill, my daughter,' he told her as he took hold of her naked bottom cheeks at the base, sinking his fingers eagerly into that succulent warm flesh, and thrust himself to the very hilt till their hairs mingled. Vigorous and strong though she was, the naked Amazon none the less had to clutch him with her arms locked round his shoulders, for she had begun to sway and to tremble at the very first dig of his prong into her quivering chasm. She closed her eyes, her nostrils opening and closing furiously as carnal desire swept through her. 'Oh, it fills me, it stretches and digs so deliciously,' she moaned in her rapture.

His lips set down at the pulse hollow of her throat as he now began to fuck her with long, deep thrusts. She let her head fall back, and her fingernails dug into his bare shoulders in her delirium.

'You are very tight, my daughter, yet there is a moistness there which tells me that you are longing for satisfaction,' he declared, without once interrupting the slow, deliberate rhythm of his coitional endeavour.

'Oh, it is true, Your Reverence. It has been many a month since I enjoyed so magnificent a cock inside me. Oh, it is so good when you push it in slowly so that I can feel every inch of it invading me and stretching me there, Your Reverence!' she gasped.

Now she began to press forward to meet his charge with an undulating twist to her ripe, full hips that showed how furiously she was being drawn toward the zenith of carnal ecstasy. Her nails dug into his flesh almost to the blood, but in retaliation his fingers squeezed and pinched the shuddering cheeks of her succulent backside. Indeed, by tactile means he was able to communicate a kind of signal to her when he meant to thrust home his blade: When his thumbs and median fingers squeezed the edges of both plump nether hemispheres, this was a sign to her that he was delving home to her hairs, whilst when he eased the grip of her behind, that meant she should be ready to expect his withdrawal.

I heard the moist, suctioning sounds which his prong and her certainly well-lubricated channel produced in this in-and-out manoeuvring. Louder grew Desirée's own gasps and sobs and sighs: 'Oh, Your Reverence, no one has ever fucked me so well. I entreat you not to stop: it is too heavenly Oh, harder! Push it into me till you tear me apart, I am strong and can endure such penance! I cannot hold on much longer, Your Reverence. Please make me spend – now – now! Oh, now!'

At this final ejaculation, raucous and sobbing, she crushed herself against him so her magnificent, naked breasts flattened against his heaving chest. At that very instant, he forced himself forward till his balls clashed against her thick, dark chestnut pubis, and with a cry of delight, announced his own fulfilment: 'Yes, now, my daughter, take it all!'

I saw her Amazonian body quake and shudder as the tempestuous burst of his essence must have lashed the foyer of her womb. Their cries coalesced, just as had their flesh and thus the most ardent widow in Languecuisse welcomed the virile English ecclesiastic.

After it was over, Father Lawrence mopped his private parts and hers with a cambric handkerchief, which he put to his nostrils, inhaling and closing his eyes with rapture. Desirée, swiftly donning skirt and blouse again, hastened to smooth down the worn cot, so that, at least by dutiful gesture and thought of hers, she would sleep better that night. Then, drawing the bolt of the door, she turned to him, her face radiant, and whispered, 'I shall knock three times, Your Reverence, after Père Mourier has begun to snore. Once he does that, I know he will not wake until the dawn.'

'Oh?' Father Lawrence chuckled. 'So, then, you have indulged his passions already, my daughter?'

'Oh no, Your Reverence! But I was told this by his last housekeeper,

Dame Clorinda, who left his service some few months ago to wed a rich widower in the village of Mirabellieu. But I am certain Your Reverence – and again I beg you to forgive me if my boldness offends you – that even if he does summon me to his bed, he cannot possibly be so competent as you in making me forget my widowhood. I bid you *au revoir*.'

Father Lawrence's door was not locked, so it was easy enough for the chestnut-haired Amazon to knock three times, slip inside and then to bolt it so that no one might interrupt their session. In a moment, she had rid herself of blouse and skirt and was Eve-naked. Licking her red lips with the tip of her nimble, pink tongue, she rubbed her flanks with nervous hands as she approached the cot on which the English ecclesiastic lay.

'What fair visitation is this?' Father Lawrence murmured as he raised his head.

'It is only myself, Your Reverence. My employer has taken to his bed and will not need me for the rest of the night. And under the law of hospitality, I wished to look in upon you and see to your comforts,' purred the handsome wench. She knelt down beside the cot, leaning toward him so that the opulent fruits of her naked bosom dangled temptingly within reach. He groped out his hand and encountered one of those luscious turrets and his fingers savouringly closed over the magnificent love-cantaloupe.

'Your hospitality is the most delicious that has ever been tendered to me, my lovely daughter,' he hoarsely murmured. 'But I would have you remember that I did not constrain you to make this sacrifice.'

'Oh, Your Reverence, it is of my own free will and eagerness. And it is no sacrifice, but rather for my own selfish pleasure. I long to feel your great cock thrusting deep within my little crevice,' whispered the beautiful, chestnut-haired widow. She now stretched out a soft hand and discovered that Father Lawrence had gone to bed in his natural state. The rigid, boldly erect structure of his sexual organ lofted between his thighs like a semaphore. It was this edifice which the charming wench first touched, as if by unerring instinct. At once her fingers closed over her prize, not wishing to relinquish it till it had performed its noble work within her cunny's valorous citadel. '*C'est incroyable!*' she breathed. 'Why, it is even bigger than the first time. You are surely more valorous than my worthy employer, who, after but a single emission of his holy fluid, acknowledged himself defeated in his desires.'

'This is the result of good English beef, daily constitutionals, long hours of meditation and a certain continence in withholding my vigour till an occasion worthy of it presents itself,' responded the English ecclesiastic. 'But I fear that this cot is far too narrow to accommodate the two of us for dalliance.'

'Oh begging Your Reverence's pardon, for I would never dare to contradict so eminent a personage as yourself, but there is a way if you will permit me to show it to you,' Desirée murmured seductively.

'I am always eager to learn new and useful knowledge, my beautiful daughter,' was Father Lawrence's riposte. At this, the naked Amazon got astride him. Though it was pitch black in this little room off the kitchen, her female instincts guided her toward what she wanted. Crouching over him, she took hold of his vigorously swollen cock with her left hand whilst, with thumb and median finger of her right, she yawned wide open the moist, pink, twitching lips of her libidinous cunt. Then, sinking down very slowly, she introduced his organ well within the warm lobby way of her matrix.

'Oh, it is hardly inside me, yet it thrills me beyond words!' she announced in her fevered and breathless whisper.

Father Lawrence lay supine at his ease, content to let the chestnut-haired housekeeper take such intimate initiative with him. Desirée sank down a little more, till the head of his throbbing organ moved just into her vaginal sheath. Then, assured that it was well within her keeping, she flattened herself over him, her big, juicy breasts mashing hard against his straining chest as his arms welcomed her, they clasping together over her satin-smooth back. Now in his turn wanting to imprison her for complete enjoyment, the English ecclesiastic spread his muscular legs and clamped them resolutely about the Amazonian widow's rippling, naked thighs. Her hands reached under his shoulders to grip him tenaciously as she groaned with pleasure to feel his massive organ dig to the very roots within her churning love-canal.

'Ah, how good it is,' she moaned. 'You pack me so tightly that my poor little spot can hardly breathe! Oh let us lie like this a long while, so that I can summon all my poor strength to deal with such a monster inside of me! Ah, I shall die of pleasure from it, Your Reverence!' the beautiful, naked widow sobbed. She fused her mouth to his and probed with her pink tongue. Her nipples were daggers of flinty-hard passion as they scraped against his heaving chest and her body was aglow with erotic energy. Now slowly, she lifted her hips a little, feeling his ramrod grudgingly recede from the innermost crannies of her hot, voracious cunt. Her groan of delirium was matched by his own gasp of rapture from the effect of this fornicatory friction. Thus stimulated, the naked housekeeper sank down to impale herself to their very hairs, and now his tongue thrust between her parted lips to fan the flames of her furious lasciviousness. The cot creaked its protest against their combined weight, but they had no heed for this whatsoever.

'What a great pity, Your Reverence,' Desirée tremulously gasped during her transports, 'that Père Mourier engaged me just before you arrived in Languecuisse! Oh, how good it is to feel you in my crevice. Oh, I beg of you, do not stop what you are doing to me – it is divine! With all respect to his holiness, I should have loved being your housekeeper instead – ah, you are bringing me close, Your Reverence!'

'Never mind, my eager daughter,' Father Lawrence gasped as he renewed his zeal, arching now to meet her wriggling exertions on his manly harpoon. 'During my sojourn in this charming village, I shall be happy to act as your confessor at any time you choose – always understanding, of course, that my worthy colleague and brother in the faith does not otherwise occupy you at the times you choose to visit me. Now, my daughter, the moment is at hand for me as well, so let me feel your responding strength!'

As he arched himself so that his furiously burdened cock could probe the deepest recesses of her Venus, Desirée uttered a shrill shriek of transported ecstasy, which the good Father promptly smothered by covering her mouth with his. Their bodies writhed and quaked in savage chaos, till at length they rolled off the cot on to the floor, where they climaxed simultaneously amid sobbing and groaning gasps of mingled rapture.

Perching on the edge of the sagging cot, I watched with growing admiration as Father Lawrence, finding himself now in command of the situation – by rolling off, he had managed to come atop and astride his beautiful mount – began to fuck her again with an even greater voracity

'Oh, Your Reverence,' Desirée breathed. 'What a marvel you are! Even though I feel your hot spunk seething in my vitals, your blade is still wonderfully hard. Oh, how it digs inside of me and finds tiny niches which it had not touched before.'

'Now hold me tightly in your beautiful arms, and clasp your firm thighs over my buttocks so that I may not become unsaddled as we ride towards our Elysian bliss together!' Father Lawrence told her.

Desirée at once complied and locked him with her magnificent, sturdy, satiny thighs, while he accelerated his thrusts till her face turned his way as a second transport neared. Once again she opened her mouth to cry out her fervent thanks for the excitement he had evoked within her loins, but the good Father silenced her as he had done before. His lips and tongue feasted on hers, and they rolled over and over on the floor as the paroxysm struck them both at the same time.

When at last tranquillity had calmed their inflamed senses, it was the Amazonian housekeeper who first cried a halt to the tryst, saying that she would fain spend the rest of the night in the arms of so demanding an employer, but must humbly beg a respite so that she might get up early at dawn to prepare Père Mourier's breakfast in his accustomed manner.

When she finally crept out of his little room, she went back to hers with the lagging step of one who is joyously fatigued. Her soft sighs were like wafting summer breezes, a sign that, for the time at least, the insatiable passions of this magnificent Amazon were satiated. As for Father Lawrence, he went back to his cot, stretched himself out on his back, pillowing his head on his arms, and fell fast asleep with a smile on his face that was doubtless an expression of the pleasure he had had in so warm a welcome to this little village in Provence.

~ 17 ~

Henriette

PAUL LITTLE 1969

All erotic and erotologic literature has one common element – authors. Without the creative human process there would be nothing to commit to the printed page. The authors of erotica are as varied as is their literary output, as has been demonstrated in previous essays. The stereotype of the 'dirty old man' pounding out smut on a cheap portable typewriter is certainly the exception rather than the rule. The workings of the creative literary mind are one of the great secrets that will probably never be understood. Otherwise anyone could be a Nobel Prize winning, bestselling author. Yet the humans behind the books are still of interest to reader and researcher alike. It is helpful to know as much about the writer as possible if one is to study as thoroughly as possible their literary output.

The last essay mentioned Paul H. Little, the world's most prolific author of erotica. Over a fifty-year period, this extraordinary man wrote more than 400 full-length erotic novels, as well as countless short stories, essays and movie scenarios on sexual themes. While the name Paul Little may not be familiar to the adult reading public, many of his nearly one hundred pseudonyms, including A. de Granamour, Ken Harding, Jack Warren, Guenter Klow, Jean Martinet, Myron Kosloff, Bruce Kemp, Hugh Jones, Lor(n)a Preston, Sylvia Sharon, Paul(a) Minton, Hugo Mentin, Paul Hugo, Hugo Paul, Paul Raymond, Harold Lambkiner, A. Vierge, and of course 'Anonymous' (especially for short stories in specialty magazines and private commission) certainly are. Additionally, Little found time to write newspaper and magazine articles on chess, travel, music and gourmet dining under his own name, but only one of his nearly three hundred additional 'legitimate' novels ever appeared with his real name on it. (*Aficionados* of mystery, adventure, historical romance and gothic novels might know Little as 'Marie de Jourlet' or 'Leigh Franklin James'.)

How could a single person write such a world's record amount of erotica, especially in the days before computer word processors? Being an expert in history and foreign languages is a start. Having a photographic memory helps, as does being simply brilliant (genius might be a better word)! Paul Little had the uncanny ability to envision entire scenes in his mind, down to the very last fine detail, and then unerringly convert these mental pictures into words. Unable, or unwilling, to type, Little dictated his stories into tape recorders and let a battery of secretaries transcribe his work. The result was usually a first and final draft that required only the most minimal editing. At his peak, Little was creating a new novel every ten days!

Paul Little was more than a human writing machine, and he defied the stereotype of the 'porno writer'. He was a suave, erudite, highly educated, charming, sophisticated, well-groomed, and generous man, who actually wrote erotica, and other novels, to supplement his salary as a copywriter and advertising executive in Chicago. His private life was actually rather mundane. He had no children, and was happily married to his first and only wife for decades until being widowed. His background though was, to say the least, unusual. Born Paul Hugo Litwinsky in Chicago in 1915, he was the son of well-to-do Jewish linen merchants. (He later changed his name and religion to avoid anti-Semitism.) Early in life he was sent with a governess to California to be educated, a circumstance that mystified him for decades, until an aunt finally informed him that his real father had not been his mother's husband! His writing talent expressed itself early on, and he was a frequent contributor to his school and college publications, often winning prizes for excellence. Sometime in 1935 or 1937, while on a visit to Chicago, he was approached by a bookseller who hired him to translate erotic French novels into English. His academic areas of expertise (literature, history and languages) made this easy money for him. It was also his first exposure to the *sub rosa* world of erotica that was to be such an important part of the rest of his life. Commissions to write original erotica followed and never stopped.

As noted, Little's primary occupation was not fiction. When not writing he even hosted a radio show. If he had any serious vices, it had to be his chain-smoking, which contributed to his death from lung cancer in 1987. Little never made a great deal of money from his erotica, and he probably continued it simply because he enjoyed it so much. Although his 'lesbian' novels, under the pseudonym of Sylvia

Sharon, were said to have sold in excess of 150,000 copies, sales of a few thousand were more typical for his brand of specialised literature. Little himself estimated he never made more than $30,000 a year from his sex writing, but he certainly made more than most erotica authors. Where the typical 'porno' author in the US might get a one-time payment of $200 to $800 for their work, the ever popular Little would receive up to $2000 as an advance against future royalties (an otherwise unheard-of situation in American 'porno' publishing). He was careful to sell only one-time rights of reproduction to his erotica, hence making it possible for him to resell his novels to other publishers at later dates (sometimes with subtle rewritings to suit his own changing tastes). Hence his *The Way of a Man with a Maid: The Sequel* first appeared as a Taurus Book in 1968, then as a Grove Press Venus Book in 1972, and then as a Grove Black Cat Book in 1979. Only two years before his death did he finally sell outright the copyrights to his erotica, all but one to this writer.

Paul Little had the facility to write in whatever style or genre his legitimate commissions required. His college majors made it easy for him to write knowledgeably and accurately on or in the style of any historical period. Strong, detailed and historically accurate descriptions, intricately described scenes and foreign phrases from up to six languages peppering the text made all his work distinctive. He was a master of descriptive prose, if a bit weak on character development. His erotica was no different. At times he was called on to create pastiche continuations for classic erotica, such as *The Way of a Man with a Maid*, *The Autobiography of a Flea* or *Maud Cameron and her Guardian*, and this he did with alacrity. Yet Little's 1960s sequels would never be confused with turn-of-the-century originals. His distinctive style was too unique.

As 'A. de Granamour', his favourite sex pseudonym (literally from the French 'a great lover'), Little developed the characteristic style that won him cult following. Novels rife with sadomasochism or spanking, occurring within historically significant settings, and frequently with the leitmotiv of chess, became his hallmark. Thousands of loyal fans awaited his next novel, bound to start with the words: 'It was the year . . . ' With de Granamour at the pen, the reader was assured fast-paced action, finely detailed scenes, a gamut of sexual activity (although never outside the realm of reality) and the sights and sounds and feel of the novel's time period. With his personal penchant for sadomasochism and spanking, Little became the premier author of these genres.

Little utilised one other talent in creating his vast *oeuvre* of erotica: translation (although in the loosest of senses). A master of European languages, an entire foreign book could be translated, and dictated, in the space of a single day. But Little never just translated. He edited and editorialised and rewrote into an American idiom or contemporary setting as he went along. He would update and modernise descriptions for the benefit of his contemporary readers. At times he would rewrite a book as he felt it should have been originally written! The end result was a literary creation as much the product of the translator as the original author.

Choosing an excerpt from Paul Little's erotica is problematic because of his frequent sadomasochistic themes and depictions. Even in his relatively 'straight' novels, such as *Passion's Vineyard* (a 1970 novel of sex and scandal in California's grape-growing region, and a possible inspiration for television's *Falcon Crest* series), there were frequent excursuses into corporal punishment. We can however here reprint a section from one of his 'translations'. The novel *Henriette* was supposedly a *c.*1960 French book first translated and printed in the US in 1969. It is a tale of the sexual awakening and initiation of a sheltered, overly protected, naïve and still virgin young Frenchwoman. In this episode, the young lady meets with her closest girlfriend, the older and more sexually experienced Simone, and together they open a new chapter in their sexual lives.

∽ from *Henriette*

It was Henriette who opened the door to Simone and murmured, 'I'm alone, my parents have already left.'

She led her friend into the salon. She was embarrassed and blushing. She both desired and feared to accomplish what she had promised.

From her point of view Simone experienced the very same desire, the same uneasiness, for they were, after all, two young women at the beginning of amorous experience.

She grew bolder, however, took Henriette in her arms and kissed her on the mouth, but without daring to slip her tongue between the girl's lips. She felt Henriette tremble against her while she gently passed her hand over the young woman's breast, and she could feel it hardening under her fingers.

'You know what you promised me?' she said. Henriette shivered.

'Show it to me now,' Simone insisted.

Henriette blushed once more and lowered her head. 'I don't dare.'

'But you must,' Simone murmured. 'I've never seen any other girl's pussy except that of my aunt. And I want to compare.' Her throat was dry with desire. She was aware that it wasn't only the need for comparison which urged her on but a much more subtle desire which she dared not yet admit. She repeated: 'Show it to me.'

'I'm ashamed.' Henriette seated herself on the divan and stared obstinately at the floor.

'You mustn't be. Take off your panties.' But the young woman remained motionless. Simone sat down beside her and gently lifted the girl's dress over her thighs, almost up to her belly. A little white slip appeared, triangular. 'Take it off.'

Henriette didn't reply. Simone gently stroked the young thighs, and her hand ascended. 'I'll help you,' she murmured, 'let me do it.'

She attained the palpitating belly and slipped down the garment. 'Get up a little, so that it will pull down better.'

And then suddenly a soft blonde fleece appeared, framing a thin pink slit.

'You mustn't,' Henriette protested as she placed her hand over her cunt. But Simone pushed it away, for a profound lascivious urge had begun to take hold of her.

'Yes, I must. You promised me. Afterwards, I'll show you mine. Now spread your legs a little.'

Henriette's pussy appeared, slightly parted and gaping. Already her clitoris was throbbing and erect.

'You see it's not so bad. Your pussy is lovely, you know. Lovelier than my aunt's, and much fresher. One day a man will plunge his prick into it, as he did into mine.'

'I don't know if – if I would let him,' Henriette faltered.

Now Simone began gently to caress the prominent pussy. She received a strange and delicious impression, the like of which she had not even dreamed of until now. And she felt the young woman tremble against her and begin to pant.

'I love to touch you, and don't you like it too?'

'I oughtn't to let you,' Henriette faltered timidly.

Simone slid her finger into the little slit and began to tickle the button of Henriette's clitoris. 'Isn't that the way you frig yourself? I'd love to make you come. Is it nice?'

'Yes.'

'You're getting wet there, you naughty girl.'

They spoke in low voices, as if they were in church, both captured in a delightful vertigo. But undoubtedly intimidated, Henriette didn't achieve orgasm. 'Show me yours too,' she said, growing bolder.

Simone let go of her, stood up and with a prompt gesture slid down her slip. Then, standing in front of her friend, she lifted her skirt to her navel, baring her smooth flat belly and the brown triangle of her sex. 'Does it please you?'

'Yes, it's lovely,' murmured the younger woman who avidly stared at her friend's pubis. 'Aside from mine, I've never seen one, you know.' She seemed to gather a little more courage and, she continued, 'And mine, I saw it because I put a mirror between my straddled legs. But that isn't comfortable.'

'Do you want to touch it?' As Henriette did not reply to this question, Simone took her hand and put it on her own pussy. At this contact, a long shudder ran through Henriette and she opened her thighs, while Simone whispered, 'You caress me too.'

The younger girl applied a timid finger and began to frig Simone. She stammered. 'It's not nice what we're doing, it's forbidden.'

'Just the same, it's very pleasant,' Simone giggled. She then seated herself near Henriette, took her into her arms and kissed the girl's neck. 'We're going to do it to each other mutually,' she proposed.

But this was extremely uncomfortable and soon Simone was taken by a brutal desire.

She pushed the younger girl back on the divan and climbed over her. 'Open your legs,' she demanded.

The younger woman no longer knew what she was doing and obeyed. Simone thrust her pussy against her friend's, and with slow movements of her loins began to rub, as she squeezed Henriette in her arms.

'Is it good now?' she whispered.

'Yes.'

However, it was an incomplete pleasure. The two women entwined. rubbed their pussies together, both bathed in sweat.

'I love you,' Simone panted. 'I wish I could be a boy to put it into you, to fuck you, to ream you. Don't you wish I were a boy?'

'Yes.'

'Would you let me fuck you?'

'I don't know,' Henriette stammered, though in the state in which she was, she would surely have been an easy prey.

'Ah,' Simone suddenly murmured, 'I want to see it, I want to see it closer.' She abandoned her prey, slipped down between the girl's thighs and then knelt down. A few inches away from her face, she saw Henriette's pussy now widely open and glistening with love-juice.

'I'm going to do to you what my uncle did to my aunt. I'm going to lick you. You'll see how good it is,' she promised.

'No,' Henriette weakly protested, 'I'm too ashamed.'

But Simone paid no attention. Her desire and curiosity overruled any other judgement. And when she planted her mouth against her friend's pussy Henriette trembled and uttered a groan.

Then Simone thrust her tongue into Henriette's slit, from upwards down and from downwards up, sometimes thrusting it into the orifice of the yawning young vagina itself.

Then she drew it back to titillate the button of the clitoris, which she finished by sucking between her lips.

Henriette's breath came more and more quickly and she began to arch and squirm. Simone paused. 'Isn't it good?' she panted.

'Yes.'

'And you're going to come, aren't you?'

'Yes.'

'I'm going to make you come very hard,' Simone said in a savage voice. 'I want to hear you cry out. We are alone, so don't hold it back.'

With this, she pressed her face back into Henriette's yawning pussy. The younger girl now began to groan. Her belly swelled and hollowed by turns. Her wrigglings became more and more feverish, as if her pussy were going forward to meet Simone's face and seek that tongue which flailed her and searched her so deliciously.

Suddenly she groaned, 'Oh, Simone!'

And all of a sudden she uttered a light cry, while love-cream seeped out of her cunt to moisten Simone's mouth and chin.

When Simone returned from the washroom, her excitement had not yet passed, and she cast a lustful gaze at Henriette's pussy.

The younger girl was still stretched out across the bed, not even thinking of hiding her nakedness. She seemed to offer her pussy to any comer.

'And now,' Simone decreed, 'you're going to do the same to me.'

'No, not that!' Henriette cried. 'It's filthy! I couldn't possibly do that!'

'Why no, since I did it to you myself. But so far as I am concerned, no one has done it to me. Don't you want to? Come on!'

Her voice grew caressing, almost pleading, and she added, 'I'd like to know what it's like.'

'No.' But now Henriette's voice was less assured.

'Yes, now stretch out, you'll see' Simone coaxed.

She put her hands on Henriette's shoulders and straddled over her in such a way that her thighs framed the younger girl's head and her pussy was almost pressed against Henriette's mouth.

'Look at my pussy, since you wanted to see it.'

'What we're doing is wrong,' Henriette stammered.

'No it isn't,' Simone declared. Then deliberately she pressed her vulva on the young woman's mouth.

'Lick me now, dear. Put your tongue into my pussy, from upwards down,' she instructed.

Clumsily, Henriette at last began to obey after a few moments of hesitation. It was a timid caress which only exasperated Simone and could not entirely satisfy her. Hence she exclaimed: 'Press harder . . . yes, like that. Up more now. Take my button into your mouth, roll it under your tongue . . . oh, that's perfect . . . oooh, it's good!'

Little shivers announced the spasms that would come upon her, and Simone panted, 'I'm going to come in your mouth darling. Go on, and don't stop above all else!'

She began to squirm her bottom to and fro, giving herself a movement of coming and going as if she were being fucked. And then suddenly, before she could hold herself back, the spasm seized her, while Henriette's hands against her bottom cheeks contracted. Perhaps Henriette was coming too. She felt a tremendous shudder run through her.

She leaned back slightly, and stiffened. 'Oh,' she cried, 'how good it is! I'm coming, I'm coming!'

Finally calm came to her while Henriette continued to lick her. 'Stop now,' she said in a languishing voice.

She got off Henriette and went back to the bathroom, taking her friend by the hand.

Henriette spat in the washbowl, and then washed her face before taking Simone's place on the bidet.

'Well,' Simone said as she kissed her friend, 'you see how nice it is with two girls together? We must start it over again, mustn't we?'

'Yes.'

'You know, the truth is,' Simone now confessed with a little smile, 'that I always wanted to do this with you, but I didn't understand what it was until yesterday. Now I can tell you, last night when I frigged myself I thought of you. And I thought I was going to see your lovely blonde pussy. And now you see how we can amuse ourselves. I know a little group of boys and girls – '

'Have you already done this with them?'

'No, because I just told you it was the first time in my life I ever did it with a girl. And with a boy – well, only one has ever fucked me, and that was just once. I think now it would be better. When I imagine a boy's cock thrusting into me, digging into my pussy, I get awfully wet. And I also get wet, now, just by looking at certain boys.' She sighed. 'We're lucky when we get excited, because it doesn't show. But with boys, when they do, their cocks stick out in their pants.'

'As for me,' Henriette said, 'I should never be able to do it with anybody else but you. I should never dare to show anybody else my pussy, much less let somebody else lick me.'

Simone kissed her. 'That's nice,' she said, 'but you won't always say that. Anyway, boys will be able to make you do it later on.'

'But I don't want them to fuck me.'

Simone shrugged. 'Come along with us, and you'll see. They won't violate you. And you can also see how other people amuse themselves. I've known them since before vacation time, but we were all virgins, apart from Maurice. We only talked about love but never did it. But now I think that since vacation time lots of thing have changed. There are three or four of us. Come tomorrow after study at seven o'clock. I'll present you to them. You'll be one of the group.'

She set a rendezvous for Henriette in a café on the Avenue Versailles.

And the next day, indeed, she presented Henriette to the group. There were two girls and two boys: Mireille, Florence, Louis and Emile. All of them were older than Henriette, who was quite cowed at first. Another boy, Guy, wasn't there. During the week he sometimes worked rather late.

All these young people went out among themselves, sometimes the girls together, sometimes a girl with a boy. Until now, apart from a few sly fondlings in the propitious shadows of the movies, a few touches on the pussy, panties that were pulled down or unbuttoned, or touches on the cock, with a hand slipped into the trousers, not much had really happened. The girls were still virgins. But the summer had passed over them and had quickly ripened them.

'My friends,' Mireille said in a triumphant tone, 'I'm a woman now.' She smiled and her eyes shone.

'I, too,' said Simone. 'What about you, Florence?'

'I'm almost one,' the girl avowed.

'The fact is,' Simone addressed them, 'that only Henriette among us is a true virgin.' She turned to her and smiled.

'We'll remedy that,' said Louis.

'No, no!' Henriette protested.

Emile shrugged his shoulders. 'They say all that and afterwards they beg for it.'

'Listen,' said Florence. 'I met Guy yesterday. Tomorrow afternoon he'll be free. We could all meet in his studio. We could have a nice long chat about all this, for I suppose that's what you really want.'

'That's right,' said Simone, 'tomorrow we don't have any classes, Henriette and I. It would be wonderful to meet that way.'

They separated and Louis, who had a good deal of money, proposed to Simone to come along in his car.

'We can have a glass of wine in a café in the Bois de Boulogne,' he said. 'You've got lots of time, since your mother comes home rather late.'

'Yes, she does, these days,' Simone agreed.

'I'm sure you don't want her to keep being without a man, young and beautiful as she is, and having to frig herself?' he slyly proposed. 'She ought to be fucked by somebody.'

'I don't care,' Simone said indifferently. They drove on for a little time in silence.

'Then it's true that this summer you lost your cherry?'

'Yes, Louis.'

'Good God! You ought to have kept it for me.'

'You never asked it of me, and besides I probably would have refused if you had. But this summer I was sort of excited. The tender grass, the weather, you know.'

'Did it hurt you?'

'A little.'

'Did you come?'

'No.'

'Because it was the first time. Later you'll come, you'll see. And did you do it again?'

'No, he just fucked me once. It was the first time I'd seen a man's cock.'

'Well,' Louis chuckled, 'just thinking about it gives me a hard-on. Look at my fly.'

Indeed, there was a thick protuberance thrusting against the crotch of his trousers. 'I must put it into you one day or another. Put your hand on it, Simone. See how hard it is.

Formerly Simone would have uttered little cries, but now without hesitating she put her hand against the swelling object.

Since the summer she had had no contact with a man's cock, and she hadn't really even touched one. And she wanted to very much.

It was a strange contact, for his cock started and throbbed, seeming to have a life all its own, and it quivered against her hand.

'Unbutton my trousers,' he murmured, 'slip your hand inside.'

She obeyed, undid his shorts, attacked the wand of flesh and caressed it, shook it gently. She felt that her pussy was tickling her and opening, that desire was heating her loins.

'Stop,' he said between clenched teeth. 'Otherwise I'll lose it. But keep holding it in your hand. You feel how hard I am?'

'I really ought to stop everything.'

'No.'

They finally arrived at the Bois. Night had fallen. Louis turned his car down a little road under the leafy trees, and stopped.

'Here we'll be quite at our ease,' he said as he turned off the lights.

'Have you already come here?'

'Yes. Take my cock out now. Caress it.'

His prick sprang out of his trousers. In the shadows, Simone saw that big white worm with a pink head which she had been holding.

He had put one arm around her shoulders and drawn her to him, he was silent and panting.

His hand lifted up her dress, slipped into her panties, attacked her furry slit and his finger dug into the crevice, while Simone opened her thighs.

This precise caress made her lose her head a little, and her gestures became disorderly. She moved the young man's cock every which way and her rhythm became incoherent.

'I'm going to put it into you,' he said. 'I'm going to fuck you. Let's go on the back seat.'

'No, not here.'

'Then suck me.'

'I've never done that.'

However, she wanted to, although the memory of the spunk which had run out of her aunt's mouth disgusted her a little. And she added, 'I don't know how.'

'Why, you can learn it easily. Take it in your mouth.'

He held her by the nape of the neck and encouraged her to lean over.

'They'll see us,' she whispered.

'No.'

They were whispering, and panting a little. Nothing else seemed to matter around them.

'Well, promise me not to go off in my mouth, then,' Simone grudgingly said.

'No, I'll warn you, and you can finish me off by frigging me.'

Simone suddenly made her decision. She bent her head down, took his prick in her hand and her mouth closed over the tip. Under her tongue, the skin of the meatus was warm and satiny. She began to suck and to titillate it.

'You see how well you do it?' he gasped.

As she was bent over, Louis slipped his hand into her panties and, while she was sucking him thus, fondled her bottom cheeks.

He separated them, and his finger introduced itself into the sticky orifice of her vulva. She arched and squirmed under this penetration, but kept sucking him. Both of them were too excited for this to last long. Louis took out his handkerchief, put it over his belly. 'Stop,' he breathed, 'I'm going to come.'

She straightened up quickly, still holding his cock in her hand.

'Frig me . . . quickly, quickly . . . aim it at my belly,' he said.

She began to shake it frantically. She felt spasms swell spasmodically and make it throb and jerk. His breath grew more hoarse and quick. 'There,' he gasped at last.

A long whitish streak spurted from the meatus, shooting even beyond his handkerchief, spotting his shirt.

Startled, Simone stopped. It was the first time she had seen a man come, or at least the first time that she had seen the sperm from his prick emerge.

'Go on,' he groaned in agony. She resumed frigging. Two other spurts, less violent, jetted out of the cock, and Louis gave a stifled groan, while his finger thrust deep into Simone's pussy.

Then his ejaculation ceased and his cock began to limpen rapidly.

'Stop,' he said. He took his handkerchief, wiped himself carefully and lingeringly, with the egotism of men, before he handed it to her, for her fingers were sticky with his sperm.

Then without a word, he buttoned himself up, while Simone pulled up her panties. He kissed her abstractedly, and then he turned on the ignition and the lights. 'You see that it went off very nicely and that no one surprised us,' he said. 'I'm going to take you back now.'

'You won't tell the others, will you?' she asked. 'It's the first time I've done it, you know. It's even the first time I've touched a boy's cock.'

'What about the one who took your cherry?'

'I only saw it when it came out of me,' was her answer.

She was afraid of being late. However, her mother came back to the house ten minutes after she did. Her mother seemed tired and her eyes were hollow with a kind of fatigue.

Bibliography

The following standard bibliographies and sources were utilised for some of the bibliographic information contained in this book.

Apollinaire, *et al.*, *L'Enfer de la Bibliothèque Nationale*, 1913

Ashbee, *Bibliography of Prohibited Books*, Brussel, New York 1962

Bécourt, *Livres Condamnés, Livres Interdit*, Cercle de la Libraire, 1961

Bilderlexicon der Erotik, Verlag für Kulturforschung, Vienna & Hamburg 1928–1931 (Supplement, 1965)

Chanover, *The Marquis de Sade: A Bibliography*, 1973

Clowes, *Bibliotheca Arcana*, Redway, 1884

Cohen–De Ricci, *Guide de l'Amateur de Livres Gravures du XVIIIᵉ Siecle*, sixth edition, 1973 reprint

Dawes, *A Study of the Erotic Literature in England*, Gothingham 1943

Deakin, *Catalogi Librorum Eroticorum*, Woolf, 1964

Englisch, *Geschichte der Erotischen Literatur*, Püttmann, 1927

Englisch, *Irrgarten der Erotik*, Lykeion, Leipzig 1931

Forbidden Books . . . by an Old Bibliophile, Carrington, Paris 1902

Fryer, *Forbidden Books of the Victorians*, Odyssey, London 1970

Fryer, *Private Case, Public Scandal*, Secker & Warburg, 1966

Galitzin Catalogue, 1887

Gay, *Bibliographie des ouvrages Relatifs à l'Amour . . .* , 1864

Gay, *Bibliographie . . .* , third edition, 1871–3

Gay–Lemonneyer, *Bibliographie . . .* , fourth edition, 1894–1900

Gillete & Dicks, *The Encyclopedia of Erotica*, Award Books, 1969

Girodias, *The Olympia Reader*, Grove Press, 1965

Girodias, *The New Olympia Reader*, Olympia Press, New York 1970

Goodland, *A Bibliography of Sex Rites and Customs*, 1931

Hayn & Gotendorf, *Bibliotheca Germanorum Erotica & Curiosa*, 1912–14 and 1929

Hoffmann, *Anglo-American Traditional Erotica*, Popular Press, 1973

Kearney, *A History of Erotic Literature*, London 1982

Kearney, *Private Case: An Annotated Bibliography*, London 1981

Kearney, *The Olympia Press: A Handlist*, London 1975

Kronhausen, *Pornography and the Law*, Ballantine, 1959

Legman, *The Horn Book*, University Press, 1964

Legman, Introduction in Kearney, *Private Case: An Annotated Bibliography*, London 1981

Marcus, *The Other Victorians*, Basic Books, 1964

Obliques, Nos. 12–13, 1977 (special de Sade issues)

Parke-Bernet Catalogue, No. 3194, *Libertine Literature*, compiled by J. B. Rund, 1971

Perceau, *Bibliographie du Roman Erotique au XIXe Siècle*, 1930

Perkins, *The Secret Record*, Morrow, 1976

Pia, *Les Livres de l'Enfer*, Coulet & Faure, 1978

Plesch, *Bibliothèque la Leonia* III, Monte Carlo 1955

Rose, *Registrum Librorum Eroticorum*, London 1936

Scheiner, *Compendium: Being a List . . .*, New York 1989

Stern–Szana, *Bibliotheca Erotica et Curiosa*, 1921

Thomas, *A Long Time Burning*, Praeger, 1969

Notes

Sources for text excerpts in *The Essential Guide to Erotic Literature*. All texts in this work are somewhat edited from any previously appearing texts, for reasons discussed in the Introduction.

1. Harris, *My Life and Loves*, 1922–7. Text from the first edition.
2. Smith (ed.), *Immortalia*, 1927. Text from the first edition.
3. Anonymous, *The Erotic Professor*, c.1930. Text from the first edition.
4. Lewton, *Grushenka*, 1933. Text from the first edition.
5. Anonymous, *Crimson Hairs*, 1934. Text from the first edition.
6. Anonymous, *The Altar of Venus*, 1934. Text from the first edition.
7. Anonymous, *Two Flappers in Paris*, c.1934. Text from the c.1935 first US edition.
8. Anonymous, *Memoirs of a Girl Student*, 1934. Text from the first edition.
9. Anonymous, *La Tarantula*, 1934. Text from the first edition.
10. Anonymous, *M. Fontaine's Establishment*, 1935. Text from the first edition.
11. Wilkinson, *An Oxford Thesis on Love*, 1938. Text from the first edition.
12. Legman *et al.*, *The Passionate Pedant*, 1939. Text from the first edition.
13. Legman *et al.*, *The Oxford Professor*, c.1940–50. Text from the first edition.
14. Nin and Friends, *White Stains*, c.1940. Text from the first edition.
15. Sewall, *The Devil's Advocate*, 1942. Text from a unique original typescript of the first edition.
16. Little, *The Autobiography of a Flea 2*, 1968. Text from the first edition. Copyright owned by C. J. Scheiner.
17. Little, *Henriette*, 1969. Text from the first edition. Copyright owned by C. J. Scheiner.

Wordsworth Classic Erotica

❧